COMMUNICATION:
from Primitive Tom-Toms to Telstar

BY G. ALLEN FOSTER

COMMUNICATION:

from Primitive Tom-Toms to Telstar

illustrated by Jack Gaughan

CRITERION BOOKS   New York

To
Thad

Acknowledgments

Clarence G. Brown, Business Manager, Laconia, N.H.,
New England Telephone and Telegraph Company,
Bell System

Miss Marguerite H. Carrig, Public Relations Department,
American Telephone and Telegraph Company,
New York City

Hon. John A. Gronouski, Postmaster General,
Washington, D.C.

CONTENTS

COMMUNICATION:
from Primitive Tom-Toms to Telstar

FOREWORD

NEARLY EVERY CLASS OF LIVING THING COMMUNICATES TO some extent. I have a huge black cat who has a different voice inflection when he demands food, asks to be petted, expresses disapproval, or merely wants attention. An earthworm is said to have a built-in radar which picks up vibrations telling him that he should come out of the ground. All animals that hunt in packs, such as wolves, have means of communication. Right now, scientists are speculating on whether porpoises have a primitive language, and Flipper has a television show with a sponsor. A dog communicates more with his eyes and tail than with his bark, but his hearing vocabulary recognizes about nine different commands.

But man can tell stories, make speeches which influence other men, command, tell old legends, bargain, make jokes, and teach. This book is the story of man's communication — from the ape man's first command to his family, to Telstar II bringing us the funeral rites of Sir Winston Churchill. Since we live in America and watch the constant advance of communication, this book moves rather quickly from the ancient origins of communication to our own front yard. It would be impossible in one volume to trace the development of newspapers, radio, telegraph, television, the telephone, and communications satellites in all parts of the world. So don't be surprised when this book jumps from Mesopotamia to Rome, to Great Britain, and suddenly lands in an American colonial tavern. We just don't have space to tell you which king of England first used the radio. We can only tell you of the day President Warren G. Harding first stepped to a microphone and broadcast his Armistice Day (now Veterans Day) address: We don't have room to discuss the effect of television on the Japanese people, but we can recall the pictures of Dallas and the next three days in Washington after the Kennedy assassination. We will go back to Sumeria, Egypt, Greece, Rome, or wherever we think some form of communication began. But we will always wind up in the United States of America.

1

THE TOWER OF BABEL

ONE FACT WE CAN BE VERY SURE OF IN THE ORIGIN OF human speech: *we know nothing about it.* Nevertheless, philologists, those people who study the history and development of language, have throughout civilized history made many attempts to explain how man began to talk. Some of their theories have merit, and others have been quite ridiculous. Let's take a look at some of them.

In the Middle Ages, explaining the origin of speech was very simple. God made speech, and he gave all

15

tribes the same language. Then the tribes got "too big for their britches," and began to build the Tower of Babel to heaven. This angered God, who took away their international language and gave them new languages, all different. It was as simple as that, the good monks said.

The French eighteenth-century philosopher Rousseau had the most naive explanation: Primitive men sat down in a kind of convention and decided what their language would be. Rousseau, as you can see, was a strong supporter of democracy, but he failed to mention in his theory what the primitive delegates to the convention used for words while they were debating what words they would have in their official language.

During the nineteenth century, three major theories were developed for the origin of language, and they are known by the strange titles, "Bow-wow," "Pooh-pooh," and "Yo-ho-ho." The followers of the "Bow-wow Theory" claimed that primitive man coined words imitative of his surroundings. "Bow-wow" of course meant *dog*. *Pow* stood for "I'll hit you over the head with my club." *Clack-clack* was the sound of an antelope's hoofs, and a gurgling sound meant *brook*. The objection to the "Bow-wow Theory" is that primitive man certainly could have done better than to imitate animal sounds. His emerging dignity and pride in being a *Homo sapiens* would have put him above quacking like a duck.

The "Pooh-pooh" philologists said that language developed in instinctive cries caused by pain or emotional sensations. Thus, the first word was probably *ouch*, followed by *oh*, and *yummy*. The "Pooh-pooh Theory" could not possibly have met the prime language needs of primitive man. His survival depended on the cooperation received in hunting and defense. "Pooh-pooh" met neither.

And finally came the followers of "Yo-ho-ho." They noted that in any strong muscular effort, such as pulling a tree with a grapevine rope, or rolling a heavy boulder, it is a relief to let out the breath suddenly. Doing this repeatedly, they said, lets the vocal cords vibrate from the breath, creating different sounds. These sounds became words such as *heave* and *haul*. The defect in this theory is obviously the same as in "Pooh-pooh."

Each of the three theories, however, explains a part of the origin of language. "Bow-wow" could have created *cuckoo* or *clang*, but not *ouch* or *heave*. Another fault in all three theories is that they assume that man was silent before he had a language, while we know that the ape men communicated effectively millions of years before *Homo sapiens*, and Flipper on his TV show adequately demonstrates the communicative powers of the porpoise.

There is one more theory which does not have a funny name: that the origin of language can be traced by watching a baby learn to make words. This is plausible up to a point. The baby makes sounds indicating hunger, anger, love, etc. But when he begins to use words, he is only copying his mother, he isn't creating a language.

And so the trail of discovering the origin of language ends here, but speculation continues. It is thought that true speech might have begun some 80,000 years ago, but we have only fragmentary information stemming from 4,000 years ago. It is considered probable that primitive man (*Homo sapiens*) relied on gestures and facial expressions more than on words. It is believed that primitive speech fell roughly into four classifications: words for objects or events (*antelope, thunder, battle*); adjectives (*fast, loud, hungry*); and command and question words (*stop, where, strike, come*). The latter class could be emphasized by gestures. There was also probably a mumbo-jumbo recital of some kind.

But although we really know nothing about the *origin* of man's language, we know a great deal about *communication* from as far back as the latter part of the Pliocene Age, millions of years ago when the ape man came down from the trees.

Great plains of grasses were just beginning to grow, and with the grasses there developed the two-toed animals with teeth adapted to chew this tough, abrasive diet. But these animals had to feed in the open fields, without the protection of the forest, and they had to develop tremendous speed to escape from the wolf, the tiger, and the newly arrived ape man. The latter had little chance of killing one of these animals by himself. To kill an antelope, the tastiest of the ape man's prey, the hunter had to have the cooperation of his family. *Cooperation* required *communication*. Communication required sounds, as well as an understanding of gestures and facial expressions.

With the necessity for greater communication than in the forest there came a strange cooperation between the ape man's tongue and his brain. The more he wagged his tongue, the more his brain grew, especially the left lobe which controls the articulation of the tongue. As this part of the brain grew, the tongue loosened, and the right hand became more deft. What the ape man could do with his now wagging tongue we of course don't know. But he certainly could emit more than a growl. If it had not been for this development in the ape man's brain he would have been forced to return to the forest and live on a vegetarian diet, or become as extinct as the dinosaur.

As these families of apes, who stood nearly upright, found that hunting together produced more food, they united with other families into tribes. Together they brought in large quantities of game and divided it. With large bands of hunters, someone had to be the "head man." Large hunts took organization. The chief had to give explicit instructions. This required more intricate communication.

As there were no tribal boundaries, tribes of ape men sometimes collided in their competition for game. Then there was a battle. The defeated had to indicate their willingness to surrender. Peace terms had to be discussed by gestures or sounds. Agreements had to be made and ratified by signs or the nodding of heads. Yes, life was becoming complicated for the ape men and their mates. It continued to get more complicated, and then, we think, a very primitive language developed with the gradual appearance of *Homo sapiens,* or primitive man, 400,000 to 700,000 years ago.

Although the first talking *Homo sapiens* remains in an historical blackout, the behavior of his twentieth century descendant should allow us to reconstruct what happened. Then as now, there must have been the "haves" and the "have-nots." Since tribal boundaries were inexact, the "have-nots" probably poached on the hunting lands of the "haves." Then there was a war. If wars were conducted 80,000 years ago as they were in earliest recorded history, the conquered were enslaved by the conquerors. Later, it would naturally follow that women of the conquered tribe would mate with some of the conquerors. To justify this assumption all we have to do is consider the number of American high school seniors who are the sons or daughters of World War II veterans who married German girls while they were serving in the Army of Occupation.

The children born to the fathers and mothers of these primitive tribes, the conquered and the conquerors, would, we assume, learn the language of both tribes, consolidate them, increasing the vocabulary of the area.

Granted that the above is pure guesswork, we can observe the growth of a language by tracing that of our own, Anglo-American. To avoid going back 4,000 years where we have meager information, let's start with the birth of Christ when the Roman Empire was under the rule of Augustus Caesar.

The Latin language had been strongly influenced by the Greeks who were enslaved by the Romans, and many of whom served as teachers. The Roman legions carried this improved language to the outskirts of the Roman Empire, which then included most of the known world. As always happens when two or more languages collide, one language has some words which describe a thing or situation better than the other. Our newspaper headlines use the French world *coup* instead of saying "The ruling government in South Vietnam was suddenly overthrown." Thus, many Latin words were adopted by the nations of Gaul (France and Belgium) and Iberia (now Spain and Portugal).

But adopted words or languages are seldom pronounced the same by the adopters. The Latin words adopted by the people of the Iberian Peninsula could not be understood by those living in that part of Gaul now called France. The Latin teacher in a public school today does not pronounce Latin the same as the parish Catholic priest.

In what we now call England, it is impossible to know what influence the Latin spoken by the Roman army of occupation had upon the ancient Celts. There are no written records in existence. But we do know that between A.D. 400 and that fateful year 1066, armed hordes from northwest Europe poured over the British Isles bringing with them new languages. The invaders were the ancestors of today's Scandinavian peoples, and they brought with them their languages which the Britons either adopted or adapted. They brought with them words which became *town, thing, house, hound, church, water,* and many others to form a language which came to be known as Anglo-Saxon.

Then came 1066, the Norman invasion, and the Battle of Hastings. William the Conqueror brought the Norman language, an ancient French based largely on Latin derivatives. Also with William came the Catholic Church and its ecclesiastical Latin. Now with William reigning over England, Norman became the language of the court and polite society.

What happened to Anglo-Saxon can be seen by looking at Chaucer's *Canterbury Tales* as originally written in 1387. The English is so different from what we speak today that only scholars can read it, but we can recognize some words even though spelling is archaic. We can also recognize words which are Latin in origin while others are obviously Anglo-Saxon. The melding was well under way. While Chaucer (1340-1400) preferred the Anglo-Saxon vocabulary, he used the Norman equivalent if the word was better for his purpose. However the influence of the Norman court was such that people who didn't speak the Norman tongue were considered country bumpkins. If you were a lady or a gentleman you didn't cling to Anglo-Saxon. Most of our so-called "dirty" words were once perfectly acceptable Anglo-Saxon words, that Chaucer used. But they gradually took on a different connotation when Anglo-Saxon was not spoken in polite society.

Here are a few typical examples of words of Anglo-Saxon and Norman-Latin origin:

Anglo-Saxon	*Norman-Latin*
wagon	ecclesiastical
boot	constitution
road	vital
bread	homicide
good	flower

Also, because the Saxons were serfs under the Normans, they associated the following words as stock and not as meat, which they seldom ate:

Anglo-Saxon	*Norman-Latin*
cow	beef
pig	pork
sheep	mutton
calf	veal

While words such as the above were melding into the English language, formal Latin was the official language of law, medicine, and the church. University classes were conducted in Latin. With this influence on the learned, we find more words of Latin origin in Shakespeare (d. 1616), and the King James version of the Bible (1611), than in Chaucer's *Canterbury Tales.* This was the English which was spoken when the *Mayflower* landed at Plymouth Rock. It would undergo drastic changes in the new land and end up as recognizable English but with a new vocabulary.

The colonists had not been long on the shore of the Atlantic Coast when an *American* language began to develop. The first settlers were immediately confronted with things and situations for which there were no English words. They couldn't very well call the birch bark *canoe* a *punt* or a *skiff*. *Hatchet* didn't adequately describe a *tomahawk*. There was no existing English word for a *catfish*. No Englishman had ever eaten corn *pone*. Englishmen didn't grow cotton, so the Americans had to invent the word *boll*. There were all kinds of vegetables and animals for which there were no English names, and to communicate, the Americans had to find new ones or borrow from their Indian neighbors. By the time Cornwallis surrendered at Yorktown, there was a difference between the English spoken in Boston and in London.

As the dislike of anything British began to grow just prior to the American Revolution, Americans deliberately changed the use of words. In doing so, they made new words, and revived archaic English word uses. They made nouns into verbs, and vice versa. To appoint a deputy became to *deputize*. To serve notice shrank to *notify*. The British shuddered. What had been a *shop* in the old country became a *store*, which had been a verb. Other changes in use and meaning of old words were *creek, shoe, lumber, corn, rock, cracker,* and *partridge*.

Following the Revolution, that most versatile of

Americans, Benjamin Franklin, proposed that studies be made for establishing a real American language. He said that getting rid of English would help to strengthen national solidarity. He also favored a strictly phonetic spelling. Franklin's friend John Adams wrote to the Continental Congress suggesting a national academy for "correcting, improving and ascertaining the English language." He said that there were such academies in France, Spain, and Italy. Adams' suggestion was not followed, but the American language grew rapidly — in the barroom, on the bench, the farm, the stump, and the schooner.

Now the American language began to feel its first foreign influence. The Dutch of Manhattan and the Hudson River Valley inserted *boss, kruller* and *stoop* (porch). The French in Louisiana brought *bayou, cache, chute, crevasse* and *levee.*

Following the War of 1812, Britishers visiting here were beginning to find part of our language incomprehensible. What was *hollowware?* Who would cook on a *spider?* And did *firedogs* bark? When did that elegant word *salon,* meaning a parlor, become a *saloon* where roughnecks drank *rotgut?* And then there were those mysterious initials: *O.K., N.G. (no good) and P.D.Q.* (pretty darned quick).

But these words and initials which nettled the British visitors were only the beginnings of an American language. Gradually, up from Mexico came *calaboose, chaparral, hacienda,* and *rancho.* As the pioneers pushed westward, and the land was divided, new "land words" grew: *lot, diggings, betterments,* and *squatter.* Old words took on new meanings such as the "think words": *calculate, expect, and reckon* — all meaning "It is my opinion."

And American slang, always colorful, always changing and usually short-lived, was zooming. Descriptive phrases which came in with the 1850's included *to darken one's door, to bark up the wrong tree* (taken from raccoon and possum hunting), *to come out at the little end of the horn* (probably a powder horn), *blind tiger* (saloon), *cold snap, long sauce, pay dirt* (from the 1849 gold rush), *small potatoes,* and *some pumpkins.*

Though by necessity the early colonists had been forced to borrow words from the Indians, the mid-nineteenth century saw even more Indian words, or translations of them, being adopted into the American language, partly because they were needed, and partly for slang or newspaper jargon. There were no English words available for *hominy, pone, toboggan, mackinaw, moccasin,* or *succotash.* These were borrowed from the Indians. But at the same time, newspapers were referring to a political conference as a *powwow.* New York's Tammany Hall was referred to in news reports as the *Wigwam,* and its boss was the *Sachem.*

Translations of Indian words were applied to American political and social life. A newspaper of 1853 might have reported: "Today, President Pierce went on the *warpath* against the Whig minority in Congress." *War paint* became slang for cosmetics. *Big Chief* was the political boss or industrial czar, and the *medicine man* was the political fixer. Two factions in a political party got together and smoked the *pipe of peace*. Then they went out and celebrated on *firewater*.

Often in the history of languages, scholars, pagan priests, and guardians of literature have tried to *put on the brakes* against new words or phrases, or have attempted to rule out of the language old words which *do the trick* but which aren't pretty. The result has always been the same. No person or group of persons can control a language or the meaning of its words. The Roman Catholic Church may be the guardian of Latin, but it wouldn't be very effective if many nations still spoke Latin daily. Scholarly Samuel Johnson attempted to standardize the English language when he published his dictionary in 1755, and he ruled out a number of words which he said were "sounds too volatile and subtle for legal restraints." But few Americans of 1780 had seen Johnson's dictionary, and couldn't have cared less. Thus they went on using *wobble, bamboozle, swap, budge, coax, touchy, stingy, fib,* and *banter,* to list just a few of the old English words which Johnson didn't like.

The frontier of Franklin Pierce's administration saw the upspring of a backwoods style in profanity and exaggeration which made a deep impression upon Mark Twain and which he recorded in his *Life on the Mississippi.* Here is an example: "Whoo-oop! I'm the original iron-jawed, brass-mounted, copper-bellied corpse-maker

from the wilds of Arkansaw! Look at me! I'm the man they call Sudden Death and General Desolation! Sired by a hurricane, dam'd by an earthquake, half-brother to the cholera, nearly related to the smallpox on my mother's side, look at me! I take nineteen alligators and a bar'l of whiskey for breakfast when I'm in robust health, and a bushel of rattlesnakes and a dead body when I'm ailin'. Cast your eyes on me, gentlemen, and lay low and hold your breath, for I'm about to turn myself loose."

The sages of Harvard, the New York *Tribune*, and the higher-ranking clergy frowned upon Mark Twain's friend, his nine alligators and his bar'l of whiskey, but the American language continued to run *hog-wild* through the nineteenth century, and no one could stop it. This was the era of industrial expansion, but it was also the era of the flamboyant politician. The extemporaneous political speaker required a half hour just to get warmed up. With still an hour or more to go, only colorful language could hold his audience. He accused his opponent of being *highfalutin'*. His campaign was *under the weather*. On most issues he was *on the fence*. He had been caught *flat-footed* buying votes — while the speaker was a *whole-souled* Democrat, and a *true-blue*, *red-blooded* American.

Up to the Civil War, American authors had generally shunned the new American language. They appeared ashamed of what they considered the vulgarity of our new vocabulary, and they were hopeful for British sales of their books. Therefore, they clung to British usage as far as they could and still be meaningful to American readers.

But during the Civil War and the years immediately following, there developed a new breed of American author. In most cases he had been a newspaper editor or reporter. He knew the language of the political rally, the gold prospector, the riverboat gambler, the revivalist preacher, and the western saloon. He knew America, he wrote about it as he saw it, and he didn't *give a hoorah* for what the British critics thought. He was Mark Twain (Samuel Clemens), Bret Harte, Petroleum V. Nasby (D. R. Locke), Artemus Ward (C. F. Browne), W. D. Howells, and Walt Whitman.

Now for the first time, the American language, as it was spoken, appeared in what would later be called literature. On the pages of these books appeared such words as *clawhammer* (coat), *to strike oil, tanglefoot* (whiskey), *hoodlum, deadbeat, grubstake, crook, sand* (courage), *slate* (political), *setback, joint* (a disreputable place), *spellbinder* (orator), *beat to a frazzle,* to *sidetrack,* to *go through* his pockets, *mule-skinner* and *wire-puller* (political manipulator). And believe it or not, Mark Twain was granted an honorary degree in England because he had *communicated* to the British the most colorful and accurate description of the American scene.

But as the American language grew, its own Tower of Babel began to crumble in spots. Within the language grew other languages — the vocabulary of industry, the various professions, the newspaper, the railroads, sports, the automobile and agriculture. Some Americans knew several of these languages, but no one knew them all. A man might know the difference between an *inning* and a *home run,* and he might know what a *galley proof* was. But if he knew these, he probably couldn't describe what a *car-knocker* did in a railroad yard, or where the *whiffletree* grew. The *city slicker* didn't know a *snath* from a *helve,* and his country cousin couldn't tell a *bull* from a *bear* on Wall Street. Nor did the farmer know that when an orchestral musician said he would have to take a piece of music *to the woodshed,* he meant he would have to give it some extra practice.

The spectacular journalism of the Hearst and Pulitzer newspapers had a marked effect on the American language between 1900 and the end of World War I. The circulation wars between these two newspaper empires called for a new kind of writing. It must be fast, tight, and colorful. In order to communicate maximum information in the least possible space, new compressed words began to appear. A merchant who charged exorbitant prices became a *profiteer.* The world of sports shrank to a *sportsdom,* and horse racing turned into *turfdom.* Places where automobiles were greased became *lubritoriums,* and a parade of automobiles was shortened to *motorcade.*

A large part of American slang is here today and gone tomorrow. But with each succeeding generation, the slang words and phrases which are most descriptive and most communicative are added to the language and become respectable. The rest become meaningless. *Twenty-three skidoo* of 1920 is an example of the latter. Few survivors of that generation can remember what it was used for. But it is hardly believable that many English teachers today would object to *cave in, fill the bill,* or *fly off the handle. Carpetbagger* of the Reconstruction period (1865-1876) describes in one word what would otherwise require a sentence, and a long one.

It is a popular belief that slang comes from the people, but the late H. L. Mencken, author of *The American Language,* disagreed. He quoted the linguistic expert Paul Shorey as saying, "The unconscious genius of the people no more invents slang than it invents epics. It is coined in the sweat of their brows by smart writers who, as they would say, are *out for the coin.*" Mencken also discounted college slang as a product of the student body. It comes, he said, from the campus wits who will probably become good newspaper men after graduation.

It is impossible for us to judge which current slang words such as *cool, square, beatnik, drag-race,* and *hootenanny* (actually a very old word) will be used by the next generation and be accepted as good Anglo-American. The durability of these words depends on whether the next generation will think up words which will better describe these things, people, and situations.

Yes, from the time the Pliocene ape man's tongue began wagging millions of years ago, language has always grown, and always will. Otherwise we would be unable to communicate in our kind of world. Bad words become good words, and vice versa. Old words take on new meanings. What if a man in 1872 had said, "I'm going to take a plane to Boston"? Had you been living then you would have assumed that the man had a job to do in Boston and was taking his tools with him, including a plane.

It would be impossible to express ourselves properly if our language did not grow from generation to generation. We must have new words for new things. What would *steam locomotive* have meant to George Washington? Nothing, because there was no need for that noun and its adjective in his time. What would General Sherman have thought if he had known that a *tank* would some day be named after him? He probably would have felt insulted. Had an aide mentioned *antiballistic missile* to General Pershing, he probably would have had the officer hospitalized for *battle fatigue,* which he knew as *shell shock.*

And so it goes, and has gone for millions of years. By the time you reach middle age, you will be using words which would be meaningless today. The dictionary is able to cope with this language explosion because words, no longer needed, are dropped with each successive edition. If you go into a Boston restaurant you will see hanging over the cash register a *Common Victualer's License. Victuals* (pronounced vittles) not so long ago meant food, but it has ceased to be used except in Boston. It is still in the dictionary, but it is marked "archaic," and probably won't remain there very long. *Cow-catcher* went out with "the iron horse." And just try asking your teacher the capacity of a *firkin*.

2

THE WRITTEN WORD

THE VILLAGE FIRE WHISTLE IS BLOWING. IT BLOWS FOUR blasts, pauses, and blows five more. It has communicated a definite message to me. First it tells me that Box 45 has been rung in, that there is a fire on North Main Street, near the shoe factory, and that all five of the fire trucks in our volunteer fire department are needed. If it repeats 45 more than three times, it means that it is a bad fire. Thus by blowing only two digits the fire whistle has given me the equivalent of twenty-six words. This certainly is compressed communication, and it is one of the oldest methods of sending messages.

Long before primitive man had developed writing, he was sending messages over long distances. Neighboring tribes, which had formed alliances against their enemies, had to have swift communications in order to rally against an attack. They soon found that a messenger on foot was too slow for safety. Probably the first instrument for the transmission of signals was a hollowed-out log which was pounded upon. Only a few signals were needed: "ENEMY APPROACHING," "COME," "I'M COMING," "ENEMY GONE AWAY." The hollowed-out log could be heard for about a quarter of a mile away if all was quiet, and the wind was in the right direction. But this required many drum stations to relay the messages in both directions and under all weather conditions.

Then something new was added, probably by accident. It could have been that a primitive man was stretching a fresh antelope skin over a hollow stump when his tiny son started pounding on it with his toy war club. The sound of the newly discovered drum could be heard farther than the hollow log. Now it was possible to send a message a mile. Fewer relay stations were needed, and fewer men were kept away from hunting. Soon it was found that a hollow log with a skin on each end performed better than the stump. As the languages of the tribes developed, more complicated signals were required, and codes were developed.

These primitive signal drums were very effective on

the grassy plains of *Homo sapiens,* and messages could be sent any distance if there were relays of drummers. But sound waves have some difficulty getting over mountains. They get over only by reflection, which is undependable. This was the problem which faced the Indians in Western America.

Smoke from campfires had always been meaningful to the Indians. It told them the direction of the wind. It indicated the barometric pressure which affected both fishing and crops. In war, the number of campfires indicated the strength of the enemy. Perhaps we should say that it was supposed to indicate the size of the opposition, since a weak tribe would undoubtedly build many campfires to deceive the enemy into thinking it was stronger than it was.

In the Western mountains, the drum or tom-tom was not practical for communication, and a more effective method was needed for spanning long distances. So the Indians again relied on their weathervane-barometer, the smoke of the campfire. Smoke signals were most effective for sending messages from one mountain peak to another. A small fire was built, and when it was roaring, wet straw was thrown on it creating a heavy, steamy smoke. The column of smoke was separated into dots and dashes by the use of a blanket held over the fire. Thus the Indian signal fire and the blanket antedated by centuries the code of Samuel F. B. Morse. Signal fires were used not only to warn of an approaching enemy or to rally aid from an allied tribe, but also in spotting game, and to keep outflung scouting parties in communication with each other.

But smoke signals were not always effective. Just as fog and battle smoke blacked out the observation balloons and signal towers of the Civil War, just so did a strong wind scramble smoke signals into gibberish. It is also possible that rival Indian tribes managed to break each other's codes, and intercept messages.

Other primitive peoples developed various forms of trumpets for transmitting signals. Large sea shells, such as that of the conch, could send vibrations at least a mile. The farmers' wives of only sixty years ago were using them to call the men in from the hayfields for dinner. Trumpets were made of elephant tusks, the horns of animals, and of wood and leather. All of these sent signals, or a code of some sort. They could warn, summon help, estimate the size of the enemy, indicate the presence of a herd of antelope, or announce a disaster. All of these messages could be delivered tersely and without fear of misinterpretation, but when time was not a factor, there was a need for more descriptive, colorful communication, and something which might be kept as a record, such as the story of the tribe's victory over its enemy, or a history of the tribe's chieftains — in other words, *Writing*.

Naturally, early man did not just sit down, write himself an alphabet, and start mailing letters to his friends. The best he could do was to draw pictures of things he wanted to communicate. For instance, he could tell a simple story by drawing a picture of crows eating up his corn and being chased away by his dog. Of course he didn't bother to draw the feathers on the crow, the tassles on the corn, or the number of his dog's teeth. Although most of his pictures represented nouns, he could change the stationary man into "man runs" by drawing the man so as to show action. His next step was to use pictures, altering them slightly, for different meanings. In Egypt, an eagle with a man's head meant *soul*. If it had an eagle's head, it naturally meant *eagle*. The American Indians drew a peace pipe for *peace*. They also drew a crude outline of a one-legged man for *cripple*, regardless of the nature of his infirmity. Again in Egypt, a picture of a man with his arm upraised, like a modern traffic officer, meant *stop*.

But to get back to the origin of writing, we first have to establish the need for it. Man doesn't often use his wits and energy to invent something unless he badly needs it. (This does not include the gadget-conscious twentieth century.) Man needed writing because he could not always rely on the old folks. Someone or something had to tell the young farmer when to plant his crops. Was it still too early, was the ground too dry, and what did an eclipse of the moon mean? If he were a coastal fisherman, he had to know when high tide would come the following week. For all this information, on which his survival depended, early man looked to the elders of the tribe. The elders relied upon their memories and their experience. They remembered how often the locust plagues came, and when they thought the time was ripe for another invasion they would warn their sons to store a surplus of food for the following year. The American Indian elders remembered that when corn was planted in poor soil it was wise to put an extra fish in as fertilizer; and that bears are to be found where there are either nuts or berries.

But as we all know, the memories of old people are not infallible. Sometimes they remember things that just didn't happen, or they exaggerate little omens into big ones over the years.

So primitive man needed something more reliable than the memory and advice of the old ones. He needed records. If he could write down the time of high tide today, the time should be about the same under the next moon. If the sun rose at a certain hour today, it should rise and set at the same time a year from today. If he did something for the first time which doubled the size of his crops, he should not rely on his memory to do the same thing next year, and he should write down the conditions of the soil and the amount of rainfall, because under different conditions his successful cultivation of the soil might not work.

Therefore, it is probable that the first writing was a primitive calendar or almanac, because it relates to primitive man's greatest concern, food. It is also probable that the first calendar or almanac was devised by tribal priests. For thousands of years, the priests, first pagan, later Hebrew, and then Christian, were the guardians of knowledge, writing, and record keeping. They were the astronomers, historians, and recorders. When man wanted information, he went to the temple. Had he himself had the information, he would not have been so dependent on the temple and the priest. The priest, with his almanac, calendar, and records of new moons, earthquakes, hurricanes, blights, floods, crop cycles, and insect pests, was indispensable to the primitive agrarian.

But for the beginnings of real writing, we have to go back to that "garden of Eden," Mesopotamia. Ancient Mesopotamia, now Iraq, lay in a lush country between the Tigris and Euphrates rivers. The people of Mesopotamia had been hunters, and then raisers of sheep. But about 5,000 years ago someone discovered how to cultivate corn. With this new source of food for the Mesopotamians, and fodder for their cattle, they settled down on farms where their cattle and sheep could be close to the crops. Next came villages, and the residents of these villagers called themselves Sumerians. Villages meant government and trade. Both needed some form of writing to keep records.

Archeologists have found a clay tablet, believed to be 5,000 years old, in one of these buried Sumerian villages. The surface of the tablet is divided into squares like a modern calendar. In each square there is a crude drawing of an object or an animal. Again, in each square there are indentations. Some are round, and others look like D's with the straight part of the letter at the top. The archeologists and experts on Sumerian history have deduced that the circles and the D's are numerals; that D meant one, and the circle, ten.

What this tablet was used for is unknown, but it obviously was used in trading: as a sales record, an inventory, or a receipt. In one square there is a circle and a picture of a calf or steer. This indicates that there were ten beef animals on hand for sale, or just sold. Another square indicates that some deal involved thirteen jugs of wine.

Gradually the Sumerian writing began to include picture words. These picture words, called pictographs, came to mean not only objects but situations and conditions. A picture of the sun and its rays might mean *sun, daytime,* or *hot.*

Eager to put into writing ideas, history, and laws, the Sumerians began developing *rebus pictographs* to spell out the syllables of their spoken words. A picture of a bee could mean *bee,* but it could also mean *to be,* thus admitting verbs to written language.

This kind of writing required an emormous number of pictographs to spell out the Sumerian language, and soon a point was reached when the Sumerian "alphabet" contained 2,000 characters. Considering our twenty-six-letter alphabet, it is obvious that Sumerian writing had become too much for the trader, and so, as usually happened in those days, and for thousands of years later, only the priests and professional scribes knew about writing. The people became as dependent upon them as they had been when the only calendar was in the temple.

This pictograph writing had its mechanical drawback.

The writing was done on a wet clay tablet with a pointed instrument which we call a *stylus*. Then the bill of sale, or receipt, was laid in the hot sun to bake. After a good sunning, the tablet was as hard as rock. Many Sumerian tablets have been found in recent years. But in drawing the pictographs, ridges of clay were pushed up, and after the clay hardened, these ridges chipped off, defacing the writing.

In order to avoid pushing out the excess clay, a wedge-shaped writing instrument was developed. Now the wet clay was pushed down, and the impressions were neat and clear after the clay hardened. But wedge-shaped impressions were ill-adapted to making pictographs, so various combinations of wedge patterns came to stand for the old pictorial symbols. *Sun* could be represented by a circle of wedges radiating out from a central axis formed by the points of the wedges. These symbols formed a kind of writing called *cuneiform*. This form of writing was used throughout the East nearly up to the birth of Christ.

While the Sumerians were learning to write, others were trying it at the same time in India, China, and Egypt. The high Sumerian civilization had crumbled after the nation was defeated in war. Egypt took the place of Sumeria as the cultured nation of the known world. It had borrowed much of its writing from the Sumerians, adding characters of its own. But the characters of Egyptian writing changed because of the writing materials. The Egyptians lacked enough high-quality clay to meet their writing needs, and so the Egyptian priests and scribes chiseled their characters into stone: granite, sandstone, and hard, black basalt. The Egyptians didn't "take his pen in hand." He took a hammer and chisel, and he thought twice before writing a letter. But if he did write a letter, it is probably lying in some museum today, 3,000 years later, as clear as the day it was written.

Because hammer-and-chisel writing was ill-adapted to the Sumerian cuneiform, the Egyptians went back to pictorial writing, but not completely. They used pictures or symbols, but these represented the letters of an alphabet and became *letter-signs*. For instance, an eagle would have been A, if they had had an A; an owl was the equivalent of M; a chicken was W, a snake was F. These letter-signs are called *hieroglyphics*.

Egyptian writers couldn't become prolific while chained to the hammer-and-chisel technique. Cleopatra wanted her mail to go out on time, and another method had to be found. The answer was growing in vast acres along the Nile River. The papyrus plant was a kind of coarse swamp grass which grew along the Nile. The Egyptians learned to remove the pith from the stalks and lay the stalks crosswise, forming sheets. To these sheets was applied a paste made from flour and water. Then the sheets were beaten until the desired thinness was obtained. Other papyrus stalks were shredded at one end and used as a writing brush with a kind of ink. Soon the Egyptians were turning out libraries of books.

The writing scene now changes to the country of Phoenicia. It was a difficult place in which to make a living. The country was hot and dry. The poor soil would support neither adequate crops nor cattle. But people lived in Phoenicia, and they had to find a livelihood, so they took to the sea. Their fast ships visited every port in the Mediterranean, even as far as the west coast of the Spanish Peninsula. They bought and sold whatever they could lay their hands on, and occasionally took time off for a little piracy.

For the Phoenician traders, the Egyptian *letter-signs* were too complicated. They needed "business writing," an alphabet as short as possible, and one which could be written swiftly. They needed an alphabet for keeping accounts, writing orders, inventories, and receipts. Therefore, they developed an alphabet in which the letters were simple lines with angles. The striking quality of the Phoenician alphabet was that it contained almost no vowels. The language contained vowels, of course, but the Phoenician reader filled them in as he read. Thus if a Phoenician trader wrote in his account book, "At Troy I purchased fifty bales of cotton," his tablet read, in Phoenician of course, "T TRY PURCHSD FFTY BLS F CTTN." Most of us could learn to read Phoenician if all we had to do was read shipping orders, but how would we make out if we had to read Longfellow's *Hiawatha* in Phoenician?

The Greeks preferred the Phoenician alphabet to the Egyptian. But Greece had her philosophers, poets, and historians. The Phoenician alphabet was not adapted to such writing. Thus the Greeks used the Phoenician alphabet as a foundation and style, but added the Greek vowels.

At the time, Egyptian papyrus was the popular writing material of the whole Mediterranean area, and Egypt was exporting tons of it. But gradually it appeared that the papyrus crops were becoming seriously depleted, and the kings placed a ban upon its exportation. Although traders had made their way to exotic China and had brought back many Chinese objects, they seem not to have noticed that the Chinese were making paper. They had been making it for years, basically the same way that we make it today. Old rags, sawdust, bark, and hemp were ground into a pulp. This "mush" was cooked and spread out on screens, making a fine paper when dried.

Not knowing about Chinese paper, the Greeks and other Mediterraneans had to look for something else. They had no plants resembling Egyptian papyrus, but sheep were plentiful. Skins were split to the desired thickness, dried, and polished with stone. Parchment is still the aristocrat of writing materials. It was bound into books, but more frequently was wound on elaborately carved scrolls. Now handwritten books began to appear in greater numbers, and more libraries sprang up, the largest at Alexandria, Egypt.

The Romans of Julius Caesar's time were a hard-headed, business-like people. Their leaders were expert administrators and great generals. Finally ruling most of the then known world, they administered their conquered territories wisely. Instead of punishing the conquered, they developed his resources and then taxed him. Instead of pillaging his gold, they brought his best ideas back to Rome. From Greece they brought sculpture, education, music, architecture, and writing. Of course they didn't borrow the whole Greek language, but they took many words from it which we use today. From their own heritage, and from the Greeks, the Romans formed an alphabet such as we use today, except that the letters J, U, and W were not used. You may wonder how Augustus was spelled without a *U*. V was used in its place — AVGVSTVS. There were no small letters, and no punctuation marks. C, D, O, Q, and B developed their present graceful curves.

The Roman alphabet came into use throughout the Empire even where much of the language did not. After the fall of Rome, the use of the Roman alphabet continued, and was adopted, even by the Vandals. However, in each country certain local changes in style occurred. This can be seen today in the difference between the type in this book and that in an old-fashioned German grammar.

Since the printing press had not yet been invented, all books were written or copied by the monks in the monasteries of the Middle Ages. This work was extremely slow and painstaking. Because the value of a book depended as much upon its beauty as upon its content, monks vied with each other in producing exquisite lettering. It soon became the custom to "illuminate" the first letter of a page or paragraph. This was written much larger than the other letters on the page, and the space within the letter was decorated with appropriate pictures, symbols, or designs. These were the first book illustrations.

In the fifth century, a young boy was captured in Gaul by the Romans and sent to Ireland as a slave. He later became converted to Christianity, entered the priesthood and, after his death, became the St. Patrick

whom we honor on the 17th of March. As Bishop Pat-
ricius, he encouraged the Irish laity to learn writing. The
Irish were so eager to write that they found the de-
tached Roman capitals too slow. Soon E became e, and
A a — letters which could be formed with one stroke of
the pen. But even this was too slow for the avid Irish.
They found no good reason for lifting their pens between
the small letters in a word, and so our present form of
cursive writing developed.

When we say so-and-so invented the first such-and-
such, we should be careful if we wish to be truthful. In
some cases, the "first" was invented so far away that the
rest of the world never heard of it, and many years later
awarded the honor for the invention to one of their own.
So it was with printing. It is generally believed that
Johann Gutenberg invented printing with movable type,
and the printing press. He did neither. The Chinese
invented printing with movable type around A.D. 105.
Gutenberg's printing press was simply an adaptation of
the coin press or any other kind of press.

The Chinese of the second century knew nothing of
the printing press, but they did carve type out of wood
blocks. Inking this wooden type, they pressed it, letter
by letter, on the paper. This was slow work, but it was
uniformly neat. A slave could be taught to print, since
he only had to follow the manuscript. The chief hazard
in Chinese printing was the alphabet of 6,000 characters
for everyday use. If the printer dropped his tray of type,
it took several days to put it back in order.

Johann Gutenberg's real achievement in originating printing with movable type in Europe came from his discovery of a metal alloy sufficiently soft to be cast into type, and hard enough to wear well. His alloy was a combination of a lead mixed with antimony and tin, and has never been substantially improved upon in 500 years. The result was the *Gutenberg Bible* which reached people who had never read the Bible before, and started the ground swell that resulted in Luther's Reformation.

The hand press hardly changed from Gutenberg's time to the days when Ben Franklin was printing *Poor Richard's Alamanac,* nor was there much change in the quality of paper. Although the Chinese had known how to make paper out of wood pulp when the Greeks were excited about Egyptian papyrus, all European paper, whether for a fine book or a newspaper, was 100 per cent rag. The chief changes in printing, from Gutenberg to the invention of the cylinder press, were in type styles, or *faces.* When a printer such as Bodoni designed a particularly beautiful type face, he ceased printing, became a type *founder,* and sold his type to other printers.

By 1482, printing presses were operating in every European city. In 1539, only twenty years after Cortez had landed, the first printing press was set up in Mexico City. The first book printed in the American colonies came off the press in 1640, *The Bay Psalm Book.*

The printer with the Gutenberg hand press could print 250 sheets an hour. With time out for lunch it would have taken him a long day to print and bind one copy of this book. But there came the Industrial Revolu-

tion in England, and the age of steam. In 1814, the London *Times* bought two steam-powered presses which could turn out 1,100 sheets an hour.

To speed up printing by steam power, a new type of press was required, a press with type mounted on a cylinder. This in turn required a new form of type, not necessarily different in face, but cast to fit the curve of the cylinder. Now the paper was fed into the cylinder from a roll, and was cut into sheets after it had come off the press. Soon it was discovered that the paper could be fed continuously through several cylinders, making it possible to print more than one page at once. Today the presses of metropolitan dailies are capable of turning out 60,000 pages an hour.

With all of the improvements in printing presses during the nineteenth century, the newspaper or book publisher couldn't ignore the fact that no matter how fast a press could print, it couldn't print until the type had been set. Typesetting hadn't changed since Gutenberg's time except for many more faces of type to choose from.

But before we come to the break-through in typesetting for the cylinder press of the nineteenth century, let's consider what the old hand press had done to the world since Gutenberg. It had printed the Bible in the native language of every European country and America. It brought the plays of Shakespeare to the stages of the English-speaking peoples. Hot off the press at Philadelphia, the Declaration of Independence was rushed out to the thirteen colonies. Printing presses turned out hundreds of thousands of copies of *Uncle Tom's Cabin*, and a decade later were printing Lincoln's Gettysburg Address. With the great decrease in illiteracy during the nineteenth century, what came off the printing press influenced the vast majority of our population.

The "break" in typesetting came in 1884 when a German watchmaker named Ottmar Mergenthaler patented a typesetting machine which revolutionized printing and publishing. He called it a *linotype*. Today you can see these linotypes in every newspaper composing room from a small-town weekly to the Atlanta *Constitution*.

The linotype is such a complex mechanism that it would take a chapter to describe it in detail. Watching this "Rube Goldberg" contraption in operation, one would guess that it could write its own editorials if required. In as few words as possible, this is what happens. The linotype operator sits before this weird machine and punches out copy on what looks like an oversize typewriter keyboard. When a key is punched, the linotype selects from its innards a metal matrix bearing the proper letter and type face. This it drops down a small chute to a frame. The next letter goes down its appropriate chute, and so on until a line has been set. The lines are automatically assembled into a page form, and on this form is pressed a thick paper matrix which serves as a mold into which is poured molten metal. Now an entire page is ready for the press. A linotype operator can set type five times faster than the manual typesetter.

We are taught in school that the vowels of our alphabet are *a, e, i, o, u* (and sometimes *y* and *w*). Each has a long and a short sound. True, these are our written vowels, but vowel sounds are something else. Probably your school choral director would agree that *e* is the only pure long vowel sound. The other spoken long vowels are all combinations. You can prove this to yourself.

Start with *a* and pronounce it very slowly. You will start with *ay*, but as you continue the sound, somewhere you will have to change to *ee* in order to finish this long vowel. Now try the same experiment with long *i*. Again you will find that you start with *ah* and finish with *ee*. Try long *o*, and you end with *oo*. The reason that Bill Rhett of South Carolina pronounces his long *i* differently from Jim Sewall of Maine is that Bill puts his emphasis on *ah*, while Jim gets to *ee* as soon as possible. But our alphabet doesn't reflect these combination vowels.

While our alphabet hasn't changed much since the reign of Julius Caesar, there is no guarantee that there won't be changes in your time. The need for a broader use of foreign languages, and for speedier reading ability in our own language, almost demands changes. Difficulties arise in learning foreign languages because the letters of the alphabet have such a wide variety of sounds. Our *j* is pronounced as in *Jackson*. But the German says *ja* (yah) for *yes*. We pronounce Mexico *Meksiko*, but with the same spelling the Mexican says *Meheeko*.

Not only do the complexities of the alphabet make it difficult for people of one nation to learn the language of another nation, but they may slow down the learning process when young Americans try to master their own language. The elementary school child learns about the letter *x*, but then finds that it has one sound in *xylophone* and another in *Timex*. The child has to learn the g of *angel* and of *angle*. If the child could tell the sound of a vowel or consonant *by just looking at it*, he might learn to read twice as fast and double his vocabulary.

Sir James Pitman, a descendant of the man who invented shorthand, believes that a new alphabet is badly needed, and he has one all ready. It contains forty-four characters instead of our twenty-six. Each character has only one sound. There can be no confusion for the child reading *said* and then *laid*. *Mike* becomes *Miek*, and *said* is spelled *sed*. This alphabet is being used by 20,000 first-graders in the United States with reportedly good results.

Our public schools are naturally hesitant to experiment with our children, and even if Sir James' alphabet produces favorable results, it may be years before it comes into wide use, if it ever does. Book publishers will shun it until practically all schools demand it. And newspapers won't use it until a Pitman-trained generation has grown up. But there may come a day when this chapter will end with *Soe long*.

3

"NEITHER SNOW NOR RAIN"

AS YOUR MAIL CARRIER PLODS HIS ROUTE ON A COLD, RAINY day, stopping at each street address to drop a small carton containing a free sample of a new detergent, no doubt he is bitter about "to-the-occupant" mailings. He must feel even sorrier for himself on the days when heavy mail-order catalogues must be delivered. But he can console himself by remembering that he cannot be required to carry a mail pouch weighing over thirty-five pounds, and his route cannot exceed a distance which requires more than eight hours for delivery. He can also get some cheer by recalling the lot of mail carriers in Babylon 4,000 years ago.

The Babylonian mail carrier delivered letters engraved on clay tablets weighting far more than today's thirty-five-pound pouch limit. The king selected young men "fleet of foot and staunch of courage" to deliver the royal mail. King Sargon the Great had a postmaster general named Urduk, whose duty it was to train these young mail carriers. Urduk also prepared a map showing every road and footpath between the Tigris and Euphrates rivers.

The Egyptians, 1,400 years before Christ, were still mailing letters inscribed on heavy tablets, written in hieroglyphics. The tablets were heavy, and the Egyptian "picture words" took up much space. But there was no real Egyptian public mail service. Anyone outside the government who knew how to write a letter paid a passing Nile boatman to deliver it for him.

The Bible's Book of Esther thus describes a "saturation coverage" mailing by Mordecai to announce the hanging of Haman: "Then were the king's scribes called at that time . . . and it was written according to all that Mordecai commanded unto the Jews, and to the lieutenants, and the deputies and rulers of the provinces which are from India to Ethiopia . . . unto every people after their language, and unto the Jews according to their writing . . . And he wrote in King Ahasuerus' name, and sealed it with the King's ring, and sent *letters by*

posts on horseback, and riders on mules, camels and young dromedaries."

King Solomon improved upon these modes of mail delivery by exchanging letters with the Queen of Sheba by means of homing pigeons.

But from the days of Solomon and Sheba to the reign of Great Britain's Queen Elizabeth I, the use of the mails was only for royalty, or in some cases for the very rich. Had those most influential mailings, Paul's Espistles to the Corinthians, been intercepted, Paul would have been put to death immediately. Uncensored mail circulating throughout the Roman Empire could cause trouble for the government, as King George III was to find out in 1775.

Carved on the facade of New York City's Post Office are the words, "Not snow, nor rain, nor heat, nor gloom of night stays these couriers from the swift completion of their appointed rounds." This inscription was placed there to describe the RFD carrier bucking Wyoming snowdrifts in his jeep, and the city carrier bowing under the barrage of a hail storm, but it was written by Herodotus in 540 B.C. He described the stalwart mail carriers of Cyrus as they carried his messages to the Persian army which was battling the Greeks.

Yes, mail carriers have always had a hard lot, but they have always been respected as rather "special" persons. From Babylon to the plains of Kansas, the mail carrier has been a representative of the nation's government. To interfere with him in his duties, or to tamper with the mail he carries has always been a serious crime.

The mail carrier was one of the pillars of the Roman Empire. Good roads permitted him to speed communications from Rome to Gaul, and the transfer stations along the mail routes became the first post offices. Only the emperor and his territorial governors could use the mail carrier, and he was their official representative. In A.D. 807, Emperor Charlemagne of the Holy Roman Empire, which was neither holy nor Roman, revived the mail system of the Caesars, and Charlemagne's system worked almost as well.

The French postal system was established by King Louis XI in 1464. His regular messengers were elaborately uniformed, and their horses' trappings sparkled with silver mountings. The messengers' arrivals were announced with flourishes on golden trumpets. To delay a royal mail carrier on his route was to risk severe punishment, even death.

Fifty-two years later, in 1516, international postal service between Vienna and Berlin became available to the wealthy. International trade was the force which drove the wedge in the mail-for-monarchs-only wall. Tradesmen needed to communicate with each other beyond the boundaries of principalities and nations. International trade, through taxes and tariffs, enriched ruling monarchs. Thus, postal service between European states was gradually permitted. However, private mail could not be carried by royal couriers. Businessmen had to engage their own carriers or entrust their mail to public coach drivers.

In England, a royal mail service was established in

1525, again restricted to governmental use. But during the reign of Good Queen Bess, a limited public mail service began to operate. This primitive postal service was carefully regulated. Post Boys rode with the mail in their saddlebags, and they carried post horns which regulations required them to blow four times in every mile. The rules of the postal service further specified that the Post Boys must ride seven miles an hour in the summer, and five in winter. Then as now, the letter-writer wished his mail to go through as rapidly as possible, and he often wrote on the envelope of his letter, "Haste, Post Haste, For Thy Lyfe, For Thy Lyfe, Haste." For further emphasis he sometimes added a crudely drawn skull and crossbones.

The Elizabethan postal system remained virtually unchanged during Elizabeth's reign, which ended seventeen years before the famous landing at Plymouth Rock. After that first brutal winter of 1620-21, the newcomers to Massachusetts Bay were homesick. They needed supplies, and they wanted to hear from home. So they wrote letters to British merchants asking them to send ships with supplies which they would pay for in furs and dried codfish. They also wrote to their friends for news of home, and they invited them to this wonderful land of plenty, without mentioning that they were near starvation. The ships, the supplies, and the immigrants came, and the ships brought mail at one penny per letter.

Richard Fairbanks of Boston is generally believed to

have been the first official postmaster in North America. By 1639, Boston had far outrun Plymouth as a community and a seaport. In that year the Massachusetts legislature designated Fairbanks' home as an official station for receiving letters. Fairbanks received one penny per letter for this service, which included meeting all incoming ships.

At the time, domestic mail service between the colonial settlements was unheard of. No one had any reason to write to anybody. The Puritans of Boston had no friends in sinful, gin-drinking Dutch New York, and there was no trade between the two towns. But by 1672, there was a need for commercial communication and correspondence between the governors of the two colonies. In that year, Governor Francis Lovelace of New York decreed that there should be a weekly mail service to and from Boston. Eleven years later, progressive Governor William Penn of Pennsylvania, wishing to "rub elbows" with the neighboring colonies, appointed one Henry Waldy "to keep a post and carry passengers between Philadelphia and Newcastle, Delaware." Waldy was to receive two pence for each letter. Now with the possibility of effective communications, a feeling of unity began to develop among the colonies, and in 1683, postal routes linked Maine with Georgia. However, these were privately operated routes, and service was sporadic.

In the meantime, Great Britain had organized a bonafide, effective mail service. The crown had finally rec-

ognized the need for domestic communications and for
mail service to and between the colonies. William and
Mary, believing that a royal mail service with the colonies would weld close bonds with the mother country,
in 1683 appointed Andrew Hamilton of New York as
Deputy Postmaster for the colonies.

Hamilton set about organizing the colonial postal service with vigor. He laid out mail routes, made arrange-
ments with tavern owners to receive mail, and made
contracts with circuit riders to carry the mail from one
station to another. Soon Hamilton had a regular royal
mail service from Portsmouth, N.H., to Williamsburg,
Va. The British Post Office considered the colonial postal
system under Hamilton to be as efficient as any in
Europe. But after Hamilton's regime, the mail service
fell upon bad days. Inefficiency and irregularity of delivery reduced confidence in the colonial postal service.
The colonists now preferred to entrust their mail to
traveling friends, and postal revenues plummeted. These
conditions continued for nearly sixty years.

Now there comes on the scene a man whose name
appears in several chapters of this book, each time in a
different capacity — Benjamin Franklin. Franklin received his appointment as Deputy Postmaster for the
colonies in 1753 and held the post for twenty-one years.

The position of Deputy Postmaster could be lucrative
in the right hands. The appointee, after paying the ex-
pense of the postal service, retained a fixed portion of
the revenue, and returned the balance to the British

Post Office. Therefore, the greater the volume of mail, the richer the Deputy Postmaster became. Hamilton had earned a very good income from the position. But his successors must have had independent incomes, for when Franklin took over the job the department was barely breaking even and returning nothing to the British government.

Under Franklin, the postal service began to boom. Franklin had a deep interest in the postal service, even though it was partly selfish. Franklin, the scientist, wanted to communicate with other scientists and scholars in the colonies and Europe. He could communicate more readily with a good post office department. Franklin enjoyed visiting other colonial scientists and inventors Also he wanted to keep an eye on the newspapers in which he had a financial interest. So what better excuse was there than the inspection of his postal routes. These trips brought him scientific information, an honorary master's degree from Harvard, and also kept his mail carriers on their toes. Soon the colonial post office department was earning Franklin a sizable income, which he did not need, and the revenue to the King was three times that of Ireland!

Franklin's motto for the colonial post office was "Expansion and Speed." Despite poor roads and great distances between population centers, Franklin stepped up mail deliveries between New York and Philadelphia from one to three times a week in summer, and from twice a month to once a week in winter. He extended post roads from Maine to Florida and from New York to Canada. Mail went to England once a month.

But with friction between King George III and the colonies rising after the passage of the Stamp Act, Benjamin Franklin had an even greater incentive for increasing the speed and efficiency of the postal service. Tempers were the hottest in Massachusetts and Virginia, and Franklin's Philadelphia was in between. When he said, "We must all hang together, or hang separately," he saw the postal service as the greatest force for hanging together. It was the most important medium for propaganda. Soon the Committees of Correspondence were at work, and the volume of mail between the colonies was zooming. Franklin, a prolific correspondent, was adding to it.

But the royal governors became aware of what was going on. Here was Franklin, an appointee of the King, using the mail service to foster rebellion. Letters went to England, and in 1774, Deputy Postmaster Benjamin Franklin was removed and a Tory appointed in his stead. But Franklin kept on writing.

Then came Paul Revere's ride, Concord and Lexington, and in 1775, Ben Franklin was appointed Postmaster General by the Continental Congress. But now his zeal in maintaining an efficient postal service was fruitless. Many mail routes were in the hands of the British, and circuit riders did not relish being captured. With General Washington maintaining his own communications system of a sort, Franklin resigned.

Following Cornwallis' surrender at Yorktown and the adoption of the Articles of Confederation, the postal service was revived for the thirteen new states. Its director was placed under the Treasury Department. It was not until 1829 that the Postmaster General became a member of the Cabinet.

Since the first weekly mail service between Boston and New York in 1672, there had been little change in the system. The only major advance was the increase in speed made possible by improved roads. The mail was carried by horse courier, packet boat, stagecoach and later by canal boats. There were no Post Office employees other than the Postmaster General, and at times a secretary. The owner of a horse or coach could bid for a contract to carry the mail between two points. The success of his bid usually depended upon his belonging to the "right" political party. The owner of a tavern or general store might agree to accept the delivery of mail. The addressees could come and get it. All contracts were only for the duration of the President's term, and all contractors were released upon a change of administration.

Early nineteenth-century postal rates were extremely high. For a one-page letter weighing less than one ounce, the rate was six cents for the first 400 miles. Twenty-five cents was charged for the same letter sent over 400 miles; and for each extra page, the rate doubled or even trebled. The heavy rag paper of the time made it a luxury to write a long letter.

Prior to 1855, it was possible to send mail "collect." The receiver of a letter could decide for himself whether the letter might be important enough to justify paying the postage. However, some mailers preferred to pay the postage in advance since they received bargain rates for doing so. Until 1847, as every stamp collector knows, there were no postage stamps. They were unnecessary for collect postage. The postmaster simply wrote the amount due on the envelope. If postage was paid in advance, the postmaster wrote "paid" on the envelope. When this became a chore, some postmasters used rubber stamps; and in some of the larger post offices, postmasters had printed their own "provisional" stamps which they pasted on letters. These "provisional" stamps are valuable today.

In 1830 there was a Maryland company called the Baltimore & Ohio Railroad. For several years it had been drawing passenger coaches with horses over a short line of track built of wooden rails covered with strap iron. But in 1831, the B & O brought out a little steam locomotive, weighing one ton, and called it *Peter Cooper's Tom Thumb. Tom Thumb* could sometimes beat a horse in a race, and it never got tired. Track mileage was increased, other steam railroad companies were organized, and Postmaster General Amos Kendall, an appointee of Andrew Jackson, became interested.

It is notable that in every form of transportation, from stage coach to jet airliner, the U.S. Post Office Department has had a large share in its promotion. Better mail service demanded better roads, and it got them. Carrying the mail brought steadier transatlantic shipping schedules. The first air mail promoted the development of commercial flying and better planes. And so it was that Amos Kendall's interest in railroads for carrying mail in the 1830's boosted the confidence of investors in expanding railroad lines and improving equipment. Even so, by the end of the decade, only a small part of the Eastern United States was linked by railroads. Travelers to California sailed to the Isthmus of Panama, crossed on donkeys' backs, and continued their sail to Yerba Buena (San Francisco).

But very few traveled to California. It was a part of Mexico, and would be for seven more years. The territory was entirely self-supporting and had no commerce. The people, all Mexican, lived a happy life, and they were so far from Mexico City that the government had pretty well forgotten that California existed, other than on the map.

Then in 1847, Mexico lost California after General Santa Anna surrendered to General Winfield Scott at Mexico City. Now United States citizens began to take some notice of their new territory. Soldiers and sailors who had been stationed there during the Mexican War remained in this sunny land, or came home to tell of the rich farm land, the good wine, and the easy life. Then came the magic word *gold,* and the gold rush of 1849 was on.

Now with California's population leaping with the

arrival of every wagon train and sailing ship, there was a pressing need for effective transcontinental mail service. At the time, the most westerly point serviced by the railroad was Tipton, Missouri. Tipton, although little more than a hamlet, was a beehive of activity. Wagon masters were busy organizing their trains for the trek to California. Emigrants from New England and New York were stocking their wagons with supplies and buying guns and ammunition. Almost every other building on the single street was a saloon, and customers were lined two deep at the bars. But prominent among the buildings on the dusty street was the office of the Butterfield Overland Mail Route. In front of its office were several rugged stage coaches built by the Abbott & Downing Company of Concord, New Hampshire. These "Concord" coaches were so sturdy that some of them are still rumbling across your TV screen today. The Butterfields had the contract to carry the U.S. Mail from Tipton to Sacramento.

In the meantime, a change had come about in the procedure for paying postal rates. The old system of sending letters collect or paying postage rates in advance, at reduced rates, had worked well for the sender and the addressee, but not for the U.S. Postal Department. It didn't cost the sender anything to mail the letter, and it cost the receiver nothing if he refused to accept it. But the delivery and acceptance cost the Post Office Department the same amount whether the mail was paid for or not. Great Britain had already solved the problem by the use of postage stamps purchased by the sender before mailing his letter.

With the end of the Mexican War, and the beginning of emigration to California, Postmaster General Cave Johnson saw that delivering letters from New York to California, without a certainty of payment, could bankrupt the Department. He appealed to Congress, and on March 3, 1847, both Houses authorized the Postmaster General to issue adhesive postage stamps. The first sheets were sold in New York City on July 1.

But postage stamps were not the answer to California's mail delivery problems. Butterfield's stage coaches were just too slow. Carrying passengers as well as mail, they stopped at frontier hotels overnight, and they stopped for dinner where there was a place to eat. While they made good time on the plains, they barely crawled when they reached the mountains, and the horses had to be rested frequently. Furthermore, the Indians were beginning to acquire firearms as well as "fire water" from the whites, and Butterfield's stage coaches were sitting ducks for an ambush.

California was no longer a territory. It had been admitted to the Union in 1850. It had senators and congressmen in Washington, and they demanded better mail service. Postmaster General Joseph Holt sat down with President James Buchanan. "Old Buck" hated making decisions. A politician rather than a statesman, he was always afraid of offending a fellow Democrat, whether a Northerner or a Southerner. There were rumblings of secession, and California seemed to be lending a sympathetic ear to the South. This probably caused Buchanan to make one of his rare decisions. He scrapped the contract with the Butterfield Overland Mail Route and inaugurated the legendary Pony Express.

The history of the Pony Express was short in days, but long in tradition, and has provided the theme for many a movie and TV western. Actually it carried the mail to California for only a year and a half. The first rider galloped out of St. Joseph, Missouri, on April 13, 1860. He did not stop to rest his horse. With his saddlebags behind him, his Colt six-guns low on each hip, and a holstered Winchester before him, he galloped on for thirty miles. When he arrived at a relay station, the mail didn't wait while he had a meal. Upon arrival, the rider tossed the saddlebags to a waiting rider, who took off immediately for the next relay station. Sometimes the

mail carrier arrived with the shaft of an arrow protruding from his shoulder. Sometimes he didn't make it at all.

The first Pony Express delivery required ten and a half days from St. Joseph to Sacramento. The fastest time was seven days and fifteen hours when the Pony Express carried a very important piece of mail — Abraham Lincoln's First Inaugural Address. But speed cost money, and the postal rates to California were at first fantastically high. A letter weighing no more than one-half ounce required five dollars in postage stamps. This was later cut to one dollar.

The Civil War and Sam Morse ended the romantic but short-lived Pony Express. The Indians, taking advantage of a divided nation occupied in setting brother against brother, stepped up their warfare. Some Indian tribes were openly allied with the Confederacy. The life of the Pony Express rider became more hazardous. Oper-

ating costs too were reaching prohibitive proportions, and yet the company which operated the Express under government contract dared not increase its rates. Then Samuel Morse's financial backers saw their opportunity, and a transcontinental telegraph line was built. Telegraph messages could be sent to and from California much cheaper than letters and poles and wires didn't cost as much as horses and men. If an Indian shot off a telegraph wire, it could be repaired, without the loss of lives. And so in October, 1861, the last Pony Express rider galloped out of St. Joe.

Until 1858, the writer of a letter, whether he lived in New York City or Ascutney, Vermont, took his letter to the post office, bought a stamp, and handed the letter to the postmaster or a clerk. But in that year, the first street letter boxes were installed in the larger cities. Now the letter-writer might have to walk only five blocks instead of fifteen. However, until 1863, although the letter-writer could now deposit his mail in a street letter box, he had to go to the post office to pick up his mail. Often there was nothing for him and the trip had been unnecessary. Most country folk waited until Saturday to get their mail. It was the day they came to town for their supplies.

Public services are rarely improved in wartime. Services require manpower, and in 1863 most of our manpower was in uniform. Nevertheless, in that year Postmaster General Montgomery Blair inaugurated free delivery of mail to residences. With a Congressional appropriation of $300,000, Blair hired 685 mail carriers who delivered mail from sixty-six post offices. Why 1863? Politicians have estimated that every patronage appointment is worth five votes among relatives and friends. There was the 1864 Presidential election coming up. It appeared that Lincoln might be in trouble, and it might be assumed that Blair's 685 new mail carriers were not McClellan Democrats.

For thirty years the railroads had been carrying the mails in increasing quantities, over ever extending routes, merely acting as a carrier. The village postmaster sorted the day's mail, put it in the proper pouches, drove his horse and buggy to the railroad station and tossed the pouches to the conductor of the passing train. The mail pouches lay in the baggage car until it reached its destination, where the mail was sorted again and put on other trains.

It was again inventive Montgomery Blair who first experimented with sorting mail on board a train running between St. Joseph and Hannibal, Missouri. Without having to sort his own mail, the Hannibal postmaster could put it on an earlier train. When the mail reached St. Joe it was sorted and ready to be carried to all points in the nation. Postmaster General Blair's system worked so well that in 1864, his successor believed that mail sorting deserved better surroundings than a corner in the baggage car. In that year, the first railroad post office, occupying a specially built car, left Chicago for Clinton, Iowa.

It was a far cry from the one-dollar postal rates of the Pony Express to the post-Civil War days when a letter could be sent to California for a few cents. But there were people who were willing to pay extra for better mail service, and in 1885 the first Special Delivery stamp was sold. There were others who were angry because they paid normal rates for less service than others paying the same rates. These were the farmers. While the city or village dweller had the mail delivered to his door, the farmer might have to drive his horse five miles to pick up a letter.

The year 1896 was an election year, and the farmers were angry about many things. Democratic Presidential candidate William Jennings Bryan was wooing the farm vote and picturing William McKinley as the tool of the rich financial interests. It was perhaps to give Bryan an "assist" that William L. Wilson, retiring President Grover Cleveland's Postmaster General, inaugurated Rural Free Delivery on October 1, 1896, one month before the Presidential election. And it probably was not by chance that Wilson started the first five experimental RFD routes in his home state of West Virginia. Today, 35,000 RFD routes serve 35,000,000 addressees.

Up to this point, we have mentioned sporadically Postmasters General from Washington's Ben Franklin to Cleveland's Wilson, omitting the tremendous changes in the duties and status of the position. Ben Franklin had an office, at times a secretary, and that was all. For over sixty years the delivery of mail was entirely by contract.

Postmasterships were political plums, doled out by the party bosses. The Postmaster General did not achieve Cabinet status until 1829. There were no full-time postal employees outside post offices until Montgomery Blair's mail carriers. Then came the railroad mail clerks in 1864, and the RFD carriers in 1896. With each of these improvements in services, the responsibilities of the Postmaster General increased.

Since 1829, the Postmaster General has been appointed by the President, with Senate confirmation, like any other Cabinet officer. However, unlike other Cabinet posts, the Postmaster General's term of office automatically expires one month beyond the term of the President by whom he was appointed. For example, Harry S. New, who was Postmaster General under Warren G. Harding, remained in office under Calvin Coolidge, but he had to be reappointed by Coolidge.

Ever since the days of Ben Franklin, the chief responsibility of the Postmaster General has been the economical and efficient operation of the Post Office Department, now the largest civilian organization of the Federal government. Reaching outside the nation, the Postmaster General negotiates postal treaties with other nations, subject to the approval of the President. Aside from directing the largest mail service in the world, he is executive head of the multi-million-dollar Postal Savings System, parcel post, and the money-order business. But the greatest pressure on every Postmaster General since 1789 has been for *speed in delivering the mails.*

There probably never has been or ever will be a time when the public was or will be satisfied with its mail service.

The United States came out of World War I with a lot of new know-how about aeronautics. The airplane was no longer confined to stunt flying at country fairs. The fragile planes flown by such aces as Quentin Roosevelt and Eddie Rickenbacker, with their cloth fuselages and spruce frames, had won battles and proved their maneuverability. Naturally after the war, with a large supply of surplus planes on hand, Postmaster General Albert Burleson seized the new opportunity for speedier mail delivery. The first experimental air mail flight was made in 1918. Regular air mail service was established between New York and Washington that same year, and to Chicago in 1919. On Washington's Birthday, 1921, an air mail plane left San Francisco on its first transcontinental flight (with refueling stops, of course) and landed at Hazelhurst Field, Long Island, New York, thirty-three hours and twenty-one minutes later. Today, air mail leaving the New York City Post Office at 9:30 P.M. arrives at Los Angeles by jet at 1:30 A.M.

In the second year of World War II, 1943, the manpower pinch was severe, and government employees in the non-defense departments had to produce the same results with less help. The sorting of mail in the great cities had always been a time-consuming, manpower-consuming problem. To speed this process, postal zones were established in 1943. The public grumbled at first, and some people refused to bother with writing zone numbers on their envelopes, but soon few hesitated to write New York 19, N.Y., because it speeded the mails.

In 1847, each person in the United States wrote about six letters a year. Of course this was an average, because some people didn't write any letters and some couldn't even write. By 1963 we were averaging 358 letters per person annually, or almost one a day. In 1962, the Post Office Department handled thirty-five billion pieces of mail!

With such a volume, it is obvious that the postal zone system begun in World War II was inadequate. After all, postal zones are designated in only 125 of our larger cities. The sorting problem was again acute. In the cities and villages without postal zones, the routing of mail took far too long to cope with the growing volume. The postal clerk in the Bullsgap, Tennessee, post office had to know the general routing for a letter going to Calais, Maine. If he didn't know, he had to take the time to look it up. There had to be an answer to this problem, and the answer went into effect on July 1, 1963. It was ZIP Code.

Prior to ZIP Code, the address on every piece of mail had to be read at least ten times. With so many readings, there was opportunity for error. In some cases ZIP Code has cut down mail delivery time by twenty-four hours. There are some 550 ZIP Code centers throughout the nation, and your community's ZIP Code number is registered with one of them. Your number enables these centers to route your mail automatically by the fastest means. ZIP Code is only 50 per cent effective unless both the sender and the person who replies to the letter use it.

Just as the telephone made the radio possible, and microwave led to Telstar, ZIP Code makes possible the electronic sorting of mail by automatic address-reading equipment. At present, the Post Office Department predicts that by 1966 most mail in large centers will be sorted electronically.

But with the population explosion of the future, there will come a time when *Mr. Zip* and his automatic address-readers will also become inadequate. It has been so ever since Governor William Penn ordered Henry Waldy to "keep a post and carry passengers." And it was only last year that an RFD carrier on St. Lawrence Island in the Bering Sea handed in his contract, unharnessed his dog sled team of Malamutes and Siberian huskies, and handed his mail pouch over to the pilot of a Piper Cub.

4

EXTRY, EXTRY, READ ALL ABOUT IT!

ON MY DESK ARE TWO NEWSPAPERS. ONE IS *The New York Times,* dated December 16, 1964. The other is the Dover (New Hampshire) *Gazette and Strafford Advertiser* of July 17, 1827. There are many similarities between these two newspapers printed 137 years apart. Both carry about the same proportion of advertising, although the *Gazette* has only four pages (one sheet folded). *The Times* has an ad for Eastern Air Lines. The *Gazette* has ads for the Dover & Portsmouth Packet Boats and the Boston Stage Line. *The Times* advertises Rheingold

Beer. The *Gazette* has an ad: "300 gallons New England Rum — John G. Tilton." Dristan Nasal Mist in *The Times* is countered by Chambers' Medicine for Intemperance in the *Gazette*. *The Times* comments on Lyndon Johnson's Inaugural Address, and the *Gazette* blasts Andrew Jackson.

But here the similarity ends. In the five-column *Gazette* there are no headlines exceeding one column in width. The left-hand column is devoted to "The Farmer's Cabinet," covering such topics as "How to Boil Potatoes Without Waste," "To Prevent Corn Being Eaten by Birds," and "The Potato Onion." There is a column reporting the proceedings of the New Hampshire legislature, and although Dover is only about forty miles from Concord, the news is ten days old. The *Gazette* leaned heavier on humor of the period than does this morning's *Times*. For instance . . .

> *The Lawyer's Declaration*
> Fee simple, and simple fee
> And all that fees entail,
> Are nothing when compared to thee,
> Thou best of fees — Feemale.

Some newspapers are justly charged with backing up advertising with news items. Perhaps the *Gazette*, in support of Chambers' Medicine for Intemperance, carried the following bulletin: "Two young ladies of the name of Stafford were recently burned to death in St. Augustine by the accidental firing of a cask of whiskey which they were drawing off with a lighted candle."

It is also noteworthy that the *Gazette* carried no news pictures. True, on the back page, in an ad for furniture, there is a picture of a table, and another ad has a picture of a bottle. These tiny pictures were bought by the *Gazette's* owner when he bought his type, and they were cast by the same process.

Newspapers were born of printers with spare time and surplus paper on their hands. When the presses were temporarily idle, the printers turned out "news letters," usually one sheet printed on one side. The London *Gazette*, founded in 1665, was the first regularly printed news sheet. It was a single sheet, printed on both sides. Its news included official government reports, with concentration on juicy scandal and crime.

The first printing press in colonial America was set up in Boston in 1638, but it was used only for job printing and book publishing. Not until fifty years later did Ben Harris publish the first newspaper in Boston. It lived for four days. Planned as a monthly publication named *Publick Occurrences Both Foreign and Domestick*, it was banned by the royal governor of Massachusetts for criticizing the British government. Here was perhaps the first time a newspaper had attempted to inform the public and influence its opinion by publishing facts.

Fourteen years later (1704), John Campbell founded the Boston *News-letter*, and employed two people besides himself. The late Will Rogers used to say, "All I know is what I read in the papers," but he would have accumulated much misinformation had he lived in 1704 and depended on Campbell's *News-letter*. Short on news, Campbell's correspondents often "faked" stories. Like the "yellow journalists" of the early twentieth century, Campbell leaned heavily on sensationalism. Pirates, who preyed along the New England coast, were his favorite subjects, and they caught the public fancy as much as the gangsters of the 1920's. Campbell's best scoop was the capture of the pirate Edward Teach (Blackbeard). But with all of his sensationalism, Campbell could sell only 250 copies of the *News-letter* a month. The illiteracy rate was high even in Boston with a population of 10,000.

John Campbell was faced with a competitor in 1719 when James Franklin, Ben's older brother, revived the *Gazette* as a weekly. America's first weekly newspaper matched Campbell's sensationalism with controversy. It was violently criticized by Rev. Cotton Mather because it opposed witch-burning. At the time, Benjamin Franklin was working for his brother as a typesetter, and he began writing a column which he signed "Silence Dogwood." One of these columns, which criticized the royal governor for negligence in chasing pirates, caused James Franklin to be thrown in jail. Benjamin continued to publish the *Gazette* for a few days until the governor closed it. Then, disliking his brother, who was still in jail, Franklin ran off to Philadelphia.

In Philadelphia, Franklin formed a partnership with a printer named Keiner, an eccentric religious fanatic, and the pair founded the Pennsylvania *Gazette*. Unable to agree on editorial policy, Keiner sold his interest to Franklin. Now Franklin demonstrated that newspaper publishing was one of his many talents which included science, diplomacy, invention, music, education, administration, and statesmanship. He was first to recognize the importance of advertising to a newspaper. The *Gazette* was so successful that at the age of forty-two Franklin retired, a rich man. Then he established the first newspaper chain in America. He encouraged his printer-editors to found newspapers in other cities. He retained a half interest in each paper, but permitted them to be editorially independent.

New York City, third in population, had its first newspaper in 1693. This poorly printed sheet had a short life, and was followed by the New York *Weekly Journal* in 1773. Its owner, Peter Zenger, a poor immigrant, was arrested and tried when he satirized a new High Sheriff of New York County, describing him in what appeared to be a classified ad:

ADVERTISEMENT

A Monkey of the larger sort, about four foot high, has lately broken his chain. Having got a War Saddle, Pistols and Sword, this whimsical creature fancied himself a General; and taking a Paper in his paw, he muttered over it, what the far greatest Part of the Company understood not.

The Sheriff read between the lines, and Zenger got a week in jail.

WHAT WERE THEY LIKE?

By 1765, every colony had one or more newspapers with the exception of Delaware and New Jersey. These papers consisted of four pages (one sheet folded in two). The pages were usually 11 x 17 inches. Most printers had no more than three *cases*, or sizes of type. Headlines were seldom used even for single columns. Most bulletins had only datelines indicating from where the story had originated. Rag paper and printer's ink were imported from England. The presses had changed but little since the days of Gutenberg. Only a small investment was required to found a newspaper, since a hand press and a case of type could be purchased for as little as $250.

All editors had first been printers. Even after he had become a highly successful publisher, Franklin still signed his name "Benjamin Franklin, Printer." The editor often set his own type, operated the press, folded the papers, and delivered them. He solicited his own advertising. When the circulation grew beyond what the editor could handle himself, he took on an apprentice typesetter. Apprentices started at age twelve and worked for only room and board until they were twenty-one. There were usually no editorials, but the papers carried "letters to the editor" on controversial subjects. The "letters" were usually written by the editor himself.

If there was a bad fire in the city, the editor ignored it. Everyone in town had been to the fire, so there was no use in reporting it. Because most of the editor's readers had family ties in England, many of the news bulletins had London datelines. Many stories, therefore, were three months old when they were printed, especially in winter when sailings were delayed. When ships failed to arrive on time, leaving the editor without enough news to fill his sheets, he "faked" harmless stories. The newspapers of 1765 carried few pictures, and these were woodcuts.

A higher literacy rate and the excitement of the French-Indian War caused newspaper circulation to rise prior to the Revolution. This is a pattern that has followed the rise of newspapers throughout the world, from Bunker Hill to Hiroshima. The average city newspaper sold 400 copies per week. This circulation would have been considerably higher were it not for the high quality of 100 per cent rag paper which permitted one newspaper to be read by many pairs of eyes before it was worn out. One copy of the New York *Journal* could serve all of the patrons of Fraunces Tavern, whereas today's newspaper doesn't last a day in a barbershop. Most newspaper subscriptions were a dollar per year, or its equivalent. Often the editor would accept meat, vegetables, liquor, and leather in lieu of cash.

As a means of public communication and information what did these pre-Revolution newspapers add up to? They brought news from Europe even though it was stale by the time it was printed. They reported the actions of the colonial legislatures. Their columns were heavily laced with crime and scandal. To some extent,

these colonial newspapers were hamstrung in fully reporting news of the royal colonial government. There
were not many John Campbells, James Franklins, or
Peter Zengers to invite jail sentences for speaking out
against governmental incompetence. But aside from
criticism of the British colonial government, the press
was free. It could inform and influence public opinion in
most fields. Definitely, fifty per cent of America was
informed because of their efforts.

The American Revolution struck the newspapers a
crushing blow at the very time when fresh news was in
the greatest demand throughout the colonies. Royalist-
sympathizing newspapers were closed in territory held
by the Yankees, and Yankee papers were driven out of
towns when the British took over. But the worst problem was paper. Great Britain had prohibited the colonies from manufacturing most products which could be
made in England, and there was not a paper mill on this
side of the Atlantic. The well-financed Connecticut
Courant built its own paper mill. George Washington
appealed to the public to save rags, and rag-saving
became a patriotic duty. Newspaper editors served as
agents in collecting rags in order that they might continue to print their papers.

With the surrender of Cornwallis, newspaper circulation in the new republic took one of its greatest leaps in
our history. There was a swift expansion of the new
paper industry. The literacy rate was rising, and in 1778,
the circulation of the Hartford *Courant* leaped to 8,000.
The year 1784 saw the appearance of the first daily

newspaper in the United States, the *Pennsylvania Packet & Daily Advertiser*. Daily newspapers had been common in England, France and Germany since 1702, but it was eighty-two years later before population centers in this country grew large enough to support dailies.

One is inclined to wonder how, even in 1784, it was possible to gather enough news for a daily paper. The answer lies in the second half of the Pennsylvania daily's title — *Advertiser*. Much of the space in this paper was devoted to market prices, ship arrivals and sailings, and their cargoes. The *Packet & Advertiser* reported all of the news it could collect, but it also served the purpose of today's *Wall Street Journal* or the financial section of a modern metropolitan newspaper.

The development of dailies had its roots in the rapidly forming political parties. Each party or party faction was represented by its newspaper. In many cities, this tended to oversaturate the newspaper market. Because politics was the prime reason for their appearance, these party newspaper editors knew no limits in slandering their political opponents. John Adams, who advocated a very strong central government, drew the following from the *National Gazette*:

> When you tell us of kings,
> And such pretty things,
> Good Mercy! how brilliant your pages!
> So bright is each line,
> I vow that you'll shine
> Like a glow-worm to all future ages.

When newspaper editors were not busy blasting the candidates of the opposing party, they took to vilifying each other. The editor of the Philadelphia *Aurora* signed his editorials "Peter Porcupine." This drew from a rival editor the comment: "As the people of America may not be informed who *Peter Porcupine* is, the celebrated manufacturer of lies, and retailer of filth, I will give you some little account of this pestiferous animal. . . ."

The time-lag in gathering news after the Revolution is best illustrated by the reporting of George Washington's death on December 14, 1799. The former President died on a Saturday night. The news was first published in the Alexandria (Virginia) *Times* on Monday morning, in the Winchester *Virginia Sentinel* on Wednesday, the Philadelphia *Aurora* on Thursday, and eleven days after Washington's death, in the Massachusetts *Spy*. The news reached the New Hampshire *Farmer's Weekly Museum* on December 30, and was finally printed in the Cincinnati *Western Spy* on January 7.

There were, of course, obvious reasons for this time-lag in news-gathering — the absence of the telegraph and the slowness of the mails. But the principal reason was the lack of a central news service. Journalism would have to wait a half century for the Associated Press. Newspapers gathered outside news by exchanging with other papers. Accordingly, the editor of the New Hampshire *Farmer's Weekly Museum* didn't learn about Washington's death until he got his copy of the Hartford *Courant*.

The end of the Revolution saw small but important technological advances in American newspaper publishing. In 1787, John Bain, a Scottish immigrant, established the first American type foundry, and the newspapers were no longer dependent on England for type. Nine years later, Adam Ramage became the first American press manufacturer. His screw press, although worked by hand, was faster than the European presses, which were still copies of the Gutenberg model.

The beginning of the nineteenth century brought with it what F. L. Mott in his *American Journalism* called "The Dark Ages of Partisan Journalism." As political parties became firmly established, newspapers became purely political organs. Even routine news was slanted. A paper might report the disbarment of an attorney as follows: "Lawyer John Doe, *an ardent champion of the Federalist cause,* was disbarred for malpractice at a recent session of the Superior Court."

Backed by partisan funds, there was a tremendous, and often suicidal growth in the number of newspapers, chiefly weeklies. The number jumped from two hundred in 1800 to twelve hundred in 1835. With the increase in the number of newspapers, there was a competitive growth in name-calling and vituperation. A Boston newspaper wrote of Thomas Jefferson: "Should the infidel Jefferson be elected to the Presidency, the seal of death is that moment set on our holy religion, our churches will be prostrated, and some infamous prostitute, under the title of Goddess of Reason, will preside in the sanctuaries of the Most High."

Such newspapers, published for the sole purpose of defeating the opposite political party, could scarcely be called organs of communication. Their columns were filled with political propaganda, pure and simple.

The excitement of the War of 1812, the burning of the White House, the battles of Lake Erie, Lundy's Lane, and New Orleans brought the first true one-column headlines, and John Bain's type foundry had to cast larger, bolder type. The Baltimore *American* published the words of Francis Scott Key's "Star-Spangled Banner." Most papers still printed only four pages, half of which was advertising.

Although the London *Times* purchased a German steam-powered press in 1814, it was not until 1825 that the New York *Gazette* purchased one of these monsters which could print 2,000 papers in an hour. But this record was soon to fall, for in 1832 the American press manufacturer, Robert Hoe, brought out a press which doubled this capacity. But type was still set for these gluttonous presses by hand. The typesetters were a sort of fraternity called "journeymen." Again to quote Mott, "They had itching feet and parched throats."

The editors of the earliest London newsletters had learned that while crime does not pay the criminal, it pays the editor, and the 1830s saw a marked increase in police court news. This from the New York *Morning Courier*: "Catherine McBride was brought in for stealing a frock. Catherine said she had just served six months on Backwell's Island, and she wouldn't be sent back again for the best glass of punch. Her husband, when she left the penitentiary, took her to a boarding house in Essex St., but the rascal got mad at her, pulled her hair, pinched her arm, and kicked her out of bed. She was determined not to bear such treatment, and so she got drunk and stole a frock, just for spite. Committed to Blackwell's Island."

Since for over a century the American public had been accustomed to waiting two months for its foreign news, and sometimes two weeks for domestic bulletins, it had not occurred to most editors that reporting a "hot" story before any other newspaper might increase circulation. But somewhere between 1830 and the Mexican War, the idea of the "scoop" took hold. It was aided by the advent of railroads, fast clipper ships, and finally the telegraph. Newspapers were now ready to spend large sums of money to scoop their rivals. British ships bound for New York were met at Halifax, Nova Scotia. The foreign news was carried to Boston by Pony Express in summer and sleighs in winter.. From Boston it was relayed to New Haven by carriage, from where it was carried by train, and sometimes special locomotive to New York. By this highly expensive route, the news could beat the British ship to Manhattan.

Then came the Mexican War, and with it another boom in newspaper circulation. This was our first war with correspondents on the scene. Without a central news service, the war correspondents of the New Orleans *Picayune* relayed their copy from the front by pony express. From New Orleans, copies of the *Picayune* were sent by horse and rail to Petersburg, Virginia, the most southerly station in Morse's telegraph company.

The Mexican War, and the service of the *Picayune,* made it obvious to a number of editors that a central news service should be established which would gather news at its source and distribute it via telegraph to newspapers which were willing to pay for the service. Morse's invention had made the "exchange system" thoroughly obsolete. The result was the founding of the Associated Press in May, 1848. The original subscribers were six New York newspapers. Soon the New York papers were joined by papers in Boston and Philadelphia. Western Union, seeing that the AP would be its best customer, leased private wires at reduced rates. Washington was brought into the network, and the AP papers had a monopoly of foreign and domestic news. Now when the President addressed Congress at noon, the editor of the *National Intelligencer* had a transcript of the address telegraphed to the New York office of the Associated Press which relayed it to the member newspapers in time for them to set type and print it for next morning's readers. This placed AP newspapers at such an advantage that non-members began to organize rival wire services. But Sam Morse recognized the AP as his best source of revenue, and Western Union refused its wires to the rival organizations. There were no antitrust laws in 1848.

The American newspaper fraternity has its three patron saints: Horace Greeley, Joseph Pulitzer, and Adolph

Horace
Greeley

Joseph
Pulitzer

William Randolph
Hearst

Ochs. It also has its patron sinner — William Randolph Hearst. What the newspaper editor, popularly known as "Go-West-Greeley," actually said was, "Go west, young man, and grow up with the country." But Horace Greeley found the end of the rainbow by coming east from a printing shop in Erie, Pennsylvania, to New York City.

Born in New Hampshire in 1811, Greeley grew up to hate farming, and signed as apprentice to a printer in East Poultney, Vermont. Finishing his apprenticeship, he obtained work with a printer in Erie, Pennsylvania, who published a weekly newspaper. But in those days of party newspapers, Greeley found that there were just too many printers in Erie. One wonders why he thought there would be any less of a surplus in New York City, but he set out for the "big town" mostly afoot and occasionally by canal boat. He arrived there on August 17, 1831, with ten dollars in his pocket, and a thorough knowledge of printing. The quality of Greeley's printing, and his energy, brought him business.

After starting two newspapers which promptly failed, Greeley entered politics, and his energies came to the attention of Thurlow Weed, then Whig boss of New York State. The 1840 Presidential campaign was wild and woolly, and in New York, Greeley's new Whig newspaper, *The Log Cabin*, had wide circulation. It was so highly regarded by William Henry Harrison's campaign managers that it was given wide circulation, and Greeley became a national figure in the newspaper

world. With Harrison elected and indebted to Greeley
for a share in his victory, a group of Whig leaders came
to Greeley with offers to invest money in a truly national
newspaper, and the New York *Tribune* was born.

Greeley was quick to sense the elements which would
draw nation-wide circulation. In his editorials he did not
confine himself to New York and Washington politics.
He wrote for farmers, and discussed their problems in
farm language. He soon had subscribers in Iowa. Greeley went out to where the news was. He sent correspondents to Washington instead of picking up congressional news from the Associated Press. When there was
talk of surveying a route for a transcontinental railroad,
Greeley traveled the proposed route by stage coach all
the way to San Francisco. Going to Europe periodically,
he visited every exposition to report new scientific
developments. During the Civil War, he sent his best
correspondents to the front, and he sent the best artists
in New York to sketch the battles. A reader of Horace
Greeley's *Tribune* was alerted to happenings everywhere
in the world.

Between the Mexican War and 1860, Greeley had
raised the circulation of the *Tribune* to 200,000. Such a
journalistic triumph was certain to affect the practices of
other editors. While they continued to state their political views in their editorials, the news ceased to be
politically slanted. Newspapers were no longer the tools
of a political party. Greeley's labor policies affected the
whole journalistic profession. He held office in the Na-

tional Typographical Union, which numbered 3,500 members in 1850. He believed in good pay for good talent, and soon editors were receiving up to $3,000 per year — no small change in 1860. Printers were averaging $12 a week, which many factory workers were earning as late as 1915. Another Greeley innovation soon caught hold — the female columnist. Women writers were hired to produce columns on fashion, etiquette, recipes, and sometimes women's suffrage.

A Confederate source was quoted as saying that the Confederacy had no need for spies while it could get the New York and Washington papers daily. And the South did receive valuable information the first two years of the war, since those papers devoted at least a third of their space to war news. The papers also printed maps and sketches of the battlefields from woodcuts.

Even though the war news coverage was excellent, it was often late in reaching the presses. This was due to the fact that telegraph lines were taken over for military use, and for the first time in our history, military censorship of news dispatches was imposed. The generals were inclined to be suspicious of war correspondents, and sometimes with reason. A reporter from the New York *Herald,* who was with General Sherman's command while the latter was preparing to attack Chattanooga, thought he had a good story when one of Sherman's officers succeeded in "breaking" the Confederate signal flag code. The correspondent's story was printed in the *Herald* which was smuggled into Richmond by Confederate spies. The Rebel code was changed just before the Battle of Kennesaw Mountain, and Sherman charged that the *Herald* story cost 10,000 Yankee lives.

At the close of the Civil War, newspapers were still being printed on rag paper, and as papers expanded beyond four pages, the cost of paper became almost prohibitive. But in Germany an inventor, Friedrich Keller, had been watching wasps making their nests by chewing up vegetable fiber. His experiments led to the discovery of a method for making paper from a combination of rags and wood pulp, and by the 1880's, rag stock had entirely disappeared. The cheaper paper increased the profits in newspaper publishing, while holding the cost down to subscribers.

Now that newspapers had expanded beyond the four-page format, their editors were crying for more news. But the war was over, and the country was relatively quiet. Not only were the editors short of news, but they lacked material for editorial comment. They could no longer praise or criticize Lincoln's conduct of the war. Even Republican editors couldn't find much to say in favor of the Grant administration, and his successor, Rutherford B. Hayes, was a colorless figure. Editors, however, had learned long ago that when there is a dearth of news, they must create it. And so the newspaper *crusade* was born. *The New York Times* battled the Tweed Ring and Tammany Hall. The Chicago *Tribune* fought the ice monopoly, and the New York

World crusaded to raise money to build the foundation for the Statue of Liberty.

The newspaper crusades proved the civic value and the power of a responsible press. The editors were able, at least temporarily, to curb municipal corruption. They helped improve the condition of the poor, and made the life of the laborer easier. And this public zeal *sold papers!* The editors poured out crusading editorials backed up by news stories. Reporters went into the slums and "sweat shops." They drank in places where the saloon-keeper operated without a license by paying off the police captain in the precinct. Artists were sent out to draw pictures (still printed from woodcuts) of unpaved streets for which paving costs had been paid, the interiors of gambling halls and opium dens. They sketched filthy orphanages, and policemen in the act of brutalizing drunks and Negroes.

Naturally, the politicians and mobsters, who were the butt of these crusades, were unhappy. Reporters were beaten, artists had their pictures destroyed, and editors' lives were threatened. But crusading developed a new kind of reporter: the young man with a nose for trouble, a yen for excitement and danger — a man who yearned to apply his writing talent to behind-the-scenes intrigue, under-the-table corruption and violence. Excellent writers developed in the crusades. The public loved the crusades, and circulation soared.

The second patron saint of journalism, Joseph Pulitzer, emerged during the era of the crusade. Honorably discharged from the cavalry after the Civil War, Pulitzer saved enough money to found a small German-language newspaper in St. Louis. Successful both as an editor and job printer, he saved $20,000 by the time he was twenty-five. In 1878, Pulitzer bought the St. Louis *Dispatch* at a sheriff's auction, and soon combined it with the *Post* to create the long admired *Post-Dispatch*.

Immediately, Pulitzer began to outcrusade the crusaders. He battled for clean streets, and against lotteries and gambling. Pulitzer was now making money fast, and his eyes turned to New York. There he bought the *World* which was losing $40,000 a year. First, he improved the layout, and then purchased new type face. In the news he leaned heavily on human interest stories with a liberal dose of scandal and crime.

Joseph Pulitzer's prescription for a successful newspaper had six ingredients:

1. Hiring the best reporters obtainable, men who wrote colorful stories.
2. Crusades and "stunts." He sponsored "Nellie Bly's" (Elizabeth Corcoran) trip around the world to beat Jules Verne's fictional *Eighty Days*. She made it in seventy-two days, six hours, and eleven minutes.
3. A liberal editorial policy.
4. A fourteen-page newspaper for two cents.
5. Increased illustration.
6. Super-promotion: billboard advertising, gift coupons, contests, puzzles, etc.

By the force of his crushing competition, Pulitzer's six points were soon the policy of every newspaper publisher who expected to remain in business.

At some time somewhere, a newspaper editor said, "A picture is worth a thousand words." But the newspapers were still held captive by the artist, the woodcut or the etched metal "cut."

The modern photoengraving process was developed by Frederic E. Ives after a series of experiments conducted at Cornell University between 1878 and 1886. Now the picture could be transferred from the camera's plate (film hadn't been invented) to a metal "cut," and from there to the press. The news photographer had been born. On May 6, 1894, the Boston *Journal,* as a stunt, printed an edition with nothing but pictures. Now, with the photoengraving process and the teletype machine in operation, only two ingredients of the present newspaper were lacking — the teletype and the telephoto process.

As the story goes, the famous Western artist, Frederic Remington, was in Havana, and the year was 1897. Remington, along with the ace war correspondent, Richard Harding Davis, had gone to Havana aboard their boss's yacht, the *Vamoose.* Their boss was William Randolph Hearst. Remington was bored, and he cabled Hearst, "THERE IS NO TROUBLE HERE — THERE WILL BE NO WAR — WISH TO RETURN — REMINGTON."

Hearst allegedly cabled his reply, "PLEASE REMAIN —

YOU FURNISH PICTURES AND I'LL FURNISH WAR — HEARST."

If anyone could have been said to have been born with a silver spoon in his mouth, it was William Randolph Hearst. Born in 1863, Hearst was the son of a silver miner who had made $7 million in the days before an income tax. The father's ambition was to have his son educated at Harvard, but Hearst's Harvard curriculum appears to have been mainly beer drinking, and he was dismissed. Disappointed in his son, but still having faith in his ability, the elder Hearst bought the San Francisco *Examiner,* and put young Hearst in charge.

William Randolph Hearst had no knowledge of newspaper publication, but he zealously set himself to studying the methods of Joseph Pulitzer. His studies paid off, and soon he was able to buy the New York *Journal* for $180,000. Following Pulitzer's principles, Hearst began hiring the best writers and cartoonists from other papers by paying higher salaries. He introduced the "sob sister" column. With this and other innovations, Hearst was soon beating Pulitzer at his own game.

But although Hearst's *Journal* and the *Examiner* were considered vulgar sheets by many newspaper men, no one could deny that the reporting was anything but the best. Hearst hired Mark Twain to cover the Diamond Jubilee of Queen Victoria. He organized two expeditions to report the Klondike gold rush. Hearst was the first publisher to give wide coverage to championship prize fights. For the Corbett-Fitzsimmons bout in 1897, he used all of his best writers, including women. In the

Hearst papers the public began to read about baseball's John McGraw, Ty Cobb, Connie Mack, and Walter Camp's great Yale football teams.

Pulitzer had been the first to use color presses to print Sunday supplements and comics. His first comic was not a "strip" in the current sense. He had a character named "The Yellow Kid." "The Kid" did not act out his escapades in a series of frames. He was spread out all over a page, shown in comic situations with other characters. "The Kid" was printed in yellow, the others in black and white. This character had no connection with Hearst but he left his name in newspaper jargon to the Hearst style which became known as "yellow journalism." Hearst's Sunday editions now included the *American Magazine,* featuring science fiction, unsolved murders, sex, and scandal.

More than one historian of journalism believes the Spanish-American War was the direct result of the circulation war between Hearst and Pulitzer. The nation was not in a mood for a war with Spain over Cuba. Mild-mannered President McKinley did not have the temperament to conduct a war. Furthermore, Spain had already capitulated on all points at issue. But Hearst was bent on having a war. Every war since we had fought the French and Indians had boosted newspaper circulation. Hearst began with editorial blasts against Spanish tyranny. Next he turned to atrocity stories. Then he managed to get one of his reporters imprisoned in Havana. Next came Davis and Remington aboard the

Vamoose. An explosion, still unsolved today, sank the U.S.S. *Maine* in Havana Harbor, and Hearst had his war.

With the rise of "yellow journalism" came a revolution in headlines. Ever since the early 1890's, headlines had often been extended to full-page width. But with the advent of the Spanish-American War Hearst headlines sometimes covered most of the front page. Wooden type was set with letters so large that often only five could be used in the width of a page. Editorial comment crept into headlines such as:

U.S.S. MAINE

SUNK IN

HAVANA

HARBOR

Public Demands

WAR!

The competition of the "yellow journalists" for screaming headlines, sensationalism, sex, scandal, and crime was certain to bring a reaction from readers who wanted dispassionate, accurate reporting of important news concerning national politics, commerce and foreign affairs. *The New York Times* approximated this in 1896, and it was losing $1,000 a day.

Adolph Ochs had started as a newsboy in Chattanooga, Tennessee. He worked as an apprentice printer, and later as a journeyman printer until he became owner of the Chattanooga *Times*. He then purchased the almost bankrupt *New York Times* for $75,000. Within twenty-five years, the paper had made $100 million. Most of this Ochs reinvested in building a great newspaper which gave its name to Times Square.

Ochs obtained the best foreign news coverage of any American newspaper by exchanging, via transatlantic cable, with the London *Times*. Och's paper rapidly became outstanding for its trustworthy reporting of Washington news. It was the first to print the full texts of Presidential speeches. *The Times* headlines were conservative, leaving more front-page space for news. The printing was outstanding, and stories were carefully edited. The reading public had confidence in Ochs and his slogan "All the News That's Fit to Print." People knew that they could depend on *The Times*.

With tension growing between the major European powers during the early summer of 1914, newspapers in the United States stepped up their foreign coverage. Then on June 28 Archduke Francis Ferdinand of Austria and his wife were assassinated in Sarajevo, Serbia. Austria, joined by Germany, declared war on Serbia. Russia and France declared war on Germany and Austria. Germany invaded Belgium, and thirty-five days after the Archduke's assassination Great Britain declared war on Germany, and World War I was full-scale reality. With the war declaration, the British War Office ordered the submarine cable from Germany to London cut. News from Germany had traveled via this cable for relay to America.

This severing of the cable no doubt gave Great Britain an edge over Germany in influencing American public opinion. However the Eastern part of the United States was definitely pro-British, and the German propaganda reaching us was arrogant and stupid, completely ignoring the temper of the American people. The sinking of the *Lusitania*, the biggest news story prior to our entry into the war, provides an example of the great weight which effective communication can have on the decisions of a great nation.

On May 7, 1915, the Cunard luxury liner *Lusitania* was torpedoed by a German submarine off the Irish Coast. Of the 1,150 passengers drowned, 114 were Americans. This led to immediate and severe protests from our government to Germany. Public opinion was seething, and war fever was high, especially in the Eastern states. Most of our news came from the British press, but the German embassy in Washington also presented the report of the German admiralty, to the effect that the *Lusitania* was known by the German admiralty to be carrying munitions, she was partially armed for anti-submarine warfare, and the German admiralty had published notices in this country that the *Lusitania* would be attacked if sighted. This did not make the headlines.

The damning evidence against Germany was that she had sunk the *Lusitania* without giving the civilian passengers a chance to take to the lifeboats. That was Germany's mistake, and *that made the headlines*. However, the *Lusitania* incident was controversial enough to bring about the resignation of President Wilson's Secretary of State, William Jennings Bryan.

The distribution of news during World War I was accelerated in 1914 when the Associated Press adopted the recently perfected teletype (see next chapter). No longer was there a row of telegraph operators in each newspaper office. AP's rival, the United Press, adopted the teletype the following year.

On the night of November 2, 1920, a Pittsburgh city editor sat beside a little box, with earphones clamped to his head. Periodically he tore his thinning hair as he listened to radio station KDKA broadcasting the Harding-Cox election returns which he would not be able to have on the street before morning. As the announcer attempted to analyze the latest returns, the city editor muttered, "All tonsils — no brains." He thought he could foresee what was in store for the American newspaper, and he was almost right. By 1930, there were 14 million radio sets in the country, and news was broadcast regularly, often on-the-spot reports. The newspapers were already suffering from the 1929 depression. Both circulation and advertising were down.

At first, both the AP and UP tried to protect their member papers by refusing their wires to radio stations. But the radio industry had risen to such power that it could afford to set up its own wire services if necessary. AP and UP capitulated, and the teletype entered the radio studio. Now the newspapers, in self-defense, began buying up radio stations, until by 1940 a third of all radio stations were owned by newspapers.

Then the newspaper-radio struggle began to come into focus. Gradually it became evident that radio newscasts did not hurt newspaper circulation. Twelve five-minute newscasts in a day could not possibly carry as much news as a twenty-four-page daily newspaper. Many editors agreed that radio helped their circulation. A listener hearing a two-minute radio bulletin of a plane crash would buy a newspaper to read about the tragedy in depth. A radio announcer could not take time to read the text of the President's message to Congress. And so the newspaper-radio war cooled off. Many papers sold their radio stations, and went back to getting out more attractive newspapers. The press and the radio industry developed mutual respect, each trying to do a better job in its own field of communication.

Tammany Hall, the name which has identified the New York County Democratic organization for over a century, brings to mind a picture of a tiger. If one were to pick up a 1928 newspaper and see a picture of a man with a big nose, smoking a cigar and wearing a derby hat, the caption would not be needed to know that the man was Presidential candidate Alfred E. Smith. And a 1936 cartoon of a man with a big jaw and a long, up-tilted cigarette holder represented Franklin D. Roosevelt.

Subway-riding newspaper readers usually scan the headlines and riffle through the paper until they reach the sports section, and many other readers with more time on their hands do the same. But somewhere in the riffling process, the reader stops for perhaps ten seconds to look at the political cartoon. Throughout the history of American journalism, the newspaper cartoon has influenced public opinion more than its editorials.

First in so many areas, Benjamin Franklin was also the first newspaper cartoonist in America. His first cartoon, a woodcut, published just before the Revolution, showed a rattlesnake cut into thirteen segments, each bearing the initials of a colony. Under the snake was the caption, "We must hang together, or we'll hang separately." The cartoon was so popular that it appeared on many regimental battle flags.

Probably the most effective political cartoonist in the history of the American newspaper was Thomas Nast of *The New York Times.* Nast was employed by *The Times* following the Civil War when the paper was crusading against Tammany Hall and the "Tweed Ring." "Big Bill" Tweed was the boss of Tammany Hall, the New York Democratic organization, and he was also the captain of the Americus Engine Company No. 6 of the New York Volunteer Fire Department. Under Tweed's control, corruption reached an all-time high in New York City. *The Times* launched a crusade against Tweed and his henchmen, and cartoonist Nast was ordered to focus his talent on Tweed and Tammany Hall.

The Americus Engine, known as "Big Six," was not only a powerful hand-pumper, but was also a gorgeous piece of equipment. Atop its pressure box was a large brass eagle holding a silver 6 in its beak. On the right and left sides of the pressure box were colorful paintings of mermaids. But on the rear of the box was a large picture of a huge snarling tiger. Thomas Nast used this menacing animal as the symbol of Tweed and Tammany Hall. The "Tweed Ring" was smashed and its boss sent to jail, but the Tammany Tiger has remained the symbol of the Democratic Political organization even in its most respectable days.

The Eighteenth (Prohibition) Amendment to the Constitution was never popular in the State of New York. The institution's greatest heckler, from the 1920's to its repeal, was Rollin Kirby of the New York *World-Telegram*. His Prohibition symbol was a ghoulish nineteenth-century undertaker who was dressed in a long black coat and a tall, stovepipe hat wrapped in crepe. On his hands the undertaker wore black "mitts" (fingerless gloves), and he always carried a bedraggled umbrella. Kirby usually drew him in a cartoon with bodies of poisoned whisky victims, gangsters, bribed federal agents, or corrupt police officers.

During the trial of New York's Mayor "Jimmy" Walker Kirby returned the Tammany Tiger to the editorial page. But this tiger was a far cry from Nast's ferocious beast. Tammany had fallen on evil days. An aroused public was defeating its candidates. Judges, police officers, and commissioners were facing jail. Now Kirby's tiger was a pitiful animal. Its tongue was hanging out with thirst. Its half-starved body could hardly stand, and its moth-eaten tail hung between its legs. Rollin Kirby was no less effective in arousing the municipal conscience than his predecessor, Thomas Nast.

But not all cartoons are funny. Some are very, very sad. Pulling at the heart strings, they sometimes remain as the finest memorial to a greatly loved man. Probably the best known and the most frequently reproduced of these is one drawn on August 17, 1935. It is a Western scene, and on a slight rise in the rangeland is a sad little cowboy with a crooked mouth, sitting on his pony. It is difficult to tell whether he is scowling or smiling, but he looks at peace as his shoulders sag. The cowboy's pony looks tired too, but he seems contented as he nibbles the sparse range grass. The figures of the cowboy and his pony are transparent, indicating that they are spirits rather than flesh and blood. The caption under the cartoon was only, "The End of the Trail." Nobody needed to be told who the cowboy was. Everyone recognized him as one of the best-loved Americans, and one of the nation's greatest humorists. Will Rogers had just been killed in a plane crash in Alaska. Just as the nation's newspaper cartoonists had powerfully reinforced the great crusades against crime and corruption, a great cartoonist, J. N. Darling ("Ding") had spoken for the nation with a pen-and-ink cartoon eulogy.

5

WHAT HATH GOD WROUGHT?

A GROUP OF BEARDED, CURIOUS POLITICIANS STOOD AROUND the strange little instrument, and the operator sitting in front of it. There was a small electromagnet with a loose steel bar suspended above it. Beside the electromagnet was a key which the operator tapped intermittently.

"You can't tell me that thing will work," said one of the onlookers.

"Course it won't," said another. "Congress just poured money down the drain when it appropriated $30,000 for

114

old Morse to build that little thing and stretch a wire all the way from here in Washington to Baltimore."

A third loafer addressed the operator, "Hey, if that thing really works, how about getting us some news from the Democratic National Convention?"

The operator nodded and started tapping on his key. Then there was silence until someone said, "So it's just like I told you."

But then the little bar atop the electromagnet began jumping up and down, making a clicking sound. The operator seized a pencil and pad, and began writing down a series of dots and dashes.

Finally the instrument was silent, and the operator began translating the dots and dashes into letters of the alphabet. When he had finished, he handed the paper to the most sarcastic of the onlookers. The skeptic glanced at the paper, slapped his forehead and said, "It's James Polk on the eighth ballot. And we got the answer in five minutes. That man Morse is a magician."

While the group was marveling at their first telegram, the operator tapped out on his key, "MESSAGE RECEIVED." At the Baltimore end of the line, facing his telegraph set, was a large man with a long, bushy beard, Samuel Finley Breese Morse. His telegraph set was placed on a table at the side of a stage over which hung a banner — 1844 DEMOCRATIC NATIONAL CONVENTION

To say that Samuel F. B. Morse was the man who invented the telegraph is an oversimplification of the truth. The same goes for most inventions and their legendary inventors. For nearly every momentuous invention in history there were dozens of scientists or tinkerers who laid the groundwork. Sometimes they discovered a theory, but couldn't see its practical application at the time. There were occasions when several inventors were working on the same invention at the same time, but separately. One of them got there first.

There is no evidence that Sam Morse knew, as he tinkered in his artist's studio, that in Russia a scientist, P. S. Jacobi, had already invented a telegraph which could send short messages. However, Jacobi's telegraph was never able to send messages long distances, never exceeding sixteen miles in his lifetime. It was Morse's telegraph which became most widely accepted in Europe.

But Morse knew that an American, Joseph Henry, had preceded him in inventing a workable telegraph. Henry blundered into science after failing as a silversmith, schoolteacher, and actor. The electromagnet had just been invented in England, and its possibilities fascinated Joseph Henry. He built a magnet larger than any produced in England, but it didn't work. There were so many wires wound around the iron core that they caused short circuits. Henry was puzzled. Little was known about insulation. Suddenly the solution to the problem flashed in Henry's mind. Off came his wife's petticoat. It was torn into strips, and Joseph Henry had the first insulated wire.

Henry's first telegraph, built in 1831, rang a bell at the

other end of a wire. His wife's petticoats depleted, he now learned to partially insulate wire with shellac. In Great Britain, an inventor named Wheatstone had also invented a telegraph while Morse was still a portrait painter.

Now, with all of these telegraphic accomplishments preceding Morse's, how can history say that Morse was the inventor of the telegraph? The answer is that not until Morse's invention, and far more important, his development of the Morse code, was there a practical telegraph for commercial and military use. The earlier telegraphs could send signals, but not letters of the alphabet. One early telegraph tinkerer tried to lick this problem by having a wire for each letter. When he pushed a key, the electromagnet at the other end of the line flashed a card with a letter printed on it. Now it is obvious that a telegraph line requiring twenty-six wires was both expensive and impractical.

At this point the reader may ask, "What did Samuel Morse have to do with the telegraph beyond inventing a code and developing a submarine cable?" Looking at the mechanical side of the question, the answer is, "Not much." The electromagnet and an electric circuit were its mechanics. Morse's experiments taught him that he could send messages over greater distances with heavier batteries, and he devised a method for sending more than one message over a wire simultaneously.

Morse's real contribution to transcontinental and trans-atlantic communication was his vision of what the telegraph could do to change the world he lived in. He dreamed of a network of telegraph lines strung all over the nation. He dreamed of linking New York with San Francisco, and Boston with London.

One dream he couldn't have had was the part the telegraph played in the Civil War. The telegraph brought the news to Washington of the bombardment of Fort Sumter, and it announced to the nation the assassination of President Lincoln. Throughout the Civil War, a network of military telegraph lines connected the War Department with every headquarters in the field. On the battlefield, a portable telegraph system took the place of today's walkie-talkie.

Samuel F. B. Morse was one of the most talented portrait painters of the early 1800's. He had studied art in England. He had painted kings, Presidents, and a huge painting of the old House of Representatives. He was recognized as successful, and in demand, but no one wanted to pay much for portraits, and he was always pressed for money. One day while Morse was in a chemist's shop, buying materials for paints, he was introduced to Joseph Henry. A friendship was born which immediately changed Morse's life. Morse had been interested in electricity, and here was America's greatest authority. Henry offered to teach Morse all he knew. Later, Morse denied this.

Borrowing money from his friends, Morse took a trip to Europe where he did some painting and studied French experiments with the electromagnet. On the return trip, with time on his hands, he worked on a telegraphic code which was to bear his name, and be used for over a century. Actually, in perfecting his telegraph, Morse was mainly borrowing from others who knew more about electricity than he. But in devising his code, not much of a feat, he had solved the one problem which had blocked the development of the telegraph as a practical means of communication. That no one else should have thought of it is almost incredible.

Back in America, Morse financed himself by teaching art at New York University. Meanwhile he was coming along rapidly with his telegraph. Now he proved to be more of a promoter than an inventor. The results of his experiments received wide publicity, so much so that the Postmaster General feared the telegraph would ruin *his* Department. Morse now went into partnership with Alfred Vail, who financed further experiments, and soon Morse was able to tap out, from one room to another, his famous message: "WHAT HATH GOD WROUGHT?"

Now, Vail and Morse were almost ready for business, but not until something had been done sufficiently dramatic to attract large investors. The 1844 Democratic National Convention was meeting in Baltimore that May. To send the proceedings of the convention over a telegraph line to Washington would cause nation-wide excitement and prove that the telegraph had a high potential for commercial use. And who would pay for the line? Uncle Sam, of course.

Morse gave a demonstration of his invention before

Congress, and got a friend, Representative David Wallace of Indiana (his son Lew wrote *Ben-Hur*), to introduce the bill subsidizing Morse to the tune of $30,000. For this, Wallace lost his seat in the next election. The bill was debated more bitterly than a present-day foreign aid appropriation. Representative Cave Johnson, in an effort to ridicule the telegraph, introduced an amendment to use half of the fund to promote Mesmerism (a form of hypnotism). Another representative moved an amendment to Johnson's amendment, providing that half of the funds for Mesmerism should be diverted to Millerism, a religious fad then prevalent. The appropriation, minus Mesmerism and Millerism, went through on a close vote of 89 to 83.

But the $30,000 which Morse and Vail received from Congress didn't carry them far. Morse decided that the wire to Baltimore should be laid underground, and Ezra Cornell built an outsize plow to do the job. The wire was laid, but it didn't work. Next a series of poles were set up, whisky bottles were used for insulators, and bare copper wire was strung. Transmission and reception were both excellent. Now Morse was a national figure, and a selfish one. He said of Joseph Henry, the man who had taught him all he knew, "I am not indebted to him for any discovery in science bearing on the telegraph."

Morse's next invention, which was his own, made national telegraph circuits possible, and finally communication with Europe. Telegraph lines could not go far without crossing rivers too wide for overhead wires. Morse now turned his attention to insulation, which everyone seems to have neglected, and the lack of which cost Morse most of his congressional appropriation. His first experimental submarine cable was laid from the Battery in New York City to Governor's Island. It was successful. Then Morse laid a cable across the Hudson River, again with success. Soon in Italy, a cable connected the mainland with Corsica.

Now the spotlight turns from Morse to a man named Cyrus W. Field. Field was a genius in business, and had made a fortune by the time he was thirty-three in 1853. In the meantime, a company had been organized to lay a cable between Nova Scotia and Newfoundland. The company had not been adequately capitalized, and was "broke." Its president, named Gizborne, came to Field looking for financial help. Cyrus Field was not a scientist, inventor, or engineer, *but he thought big*. Looking at the globe, he probably said, "Why fool around with Newfoundland? Let's lay her straight to Europe."

For advice, Field consulted Matthew Maury of the U.S. Navy, the man who knew more about the ocean bottom than anyone else in the world. Maury showed Field where to lay the cable, avoiding the Atlantic's greatest depths, as well as the threat of icebergs. Then Field went to Sam Morse. Morse was convinced that an electrical current could be sent from Newfoundland to England. A company was formed: The New York, New-foundland, and London Telegraph Company.

The project took thirteen years, and $12 million, for completion. Field was required to go to London forty times, and each one-way trip took a month. First, Field found that sailing ships, lacking complete maneuverability, could not be used for laying cable. And there were no steam vessels available at the time that could be chartered for the slow task of cable-laying.

In 1856, Field made one of his trips to London where he saw the *Great Eastern,* five times the size of any steamship ever built, under construction. If I could only have her to lay the cable, he thought. A clever negotiator, Field worked out an agreement with the United States and British governments that each would supply a warship to lay the cable. The two ships would meet in the mid-Atlantic, and the cable would be spliced. At the same time, Morse made an important improvement in his cable. Gutta-percha had been discovered, a substance much like rubber but more resinous. It made excellent insulating material. Now the cable-laying began. The British Warship H.M.S. *Agamemnon* was only 335 miles out when an engineer applied a brake to the cable drum too quickly. The cable snapped, and now 355 miles of it lay at the bottom of the ocean. This was but the first in a series of disasters which would have broken the spirit of most men.

But Cyrus Field set about reorganizing his comany and raising new funds. Another cable was built, and in 1858, the cable ships sailed out from New York and Ireland. In spite of bad storms, the two ships made their rendezvous. The cable was spliced. It snapped. They spliced it again, and again it broke. On the third try, the splice was successful, and the first transatlantic cable sank to the ocean floor. Field was a hero. His name was toasted on both sides of the Atlantic, and babies were named after him. Surplus cable was cut into small lengths and sold as souvenirs at Tiffany's. Messages were pouring over the cable to and from London. Then the cable went dead.

For a year, the cable had been exposed to the sun on the docks at Plymouth, England, and the gutta-percha had rotted. Furthermore, the cable drums had rolled around in the hull of the *Agamemnon* until some of the gutta-percha had been damaged. It is a wonder that the cable lasted as long as it did.

By now, Field's fortune had been exhausted. Every dollar of American capital was needed to prosecute the Civil War, and Field had to look to Europe for money to build and lay a new cable. The *Great Eastern,* with her six funnels, had been completed, and she had made her maiden voyage. But Field now found her lying idle at her dock. She was just too big for that period. The demand for transatlantic passage was not enough to make the *Great Eastern* profitable. Field made a deal with her owners. If the *Great Eastern* would lay the cable successfully, Field would give her owners $250,000 in his company's stock. If the cable was not laid, they would get nothing. The cable was loaded aboard the *Great Eastern,* and again it broke in mid-ocean.

With the cable broken, and Field broken financially, that should have put an end to the cable business. But Cyrus Field was not that kind of man. The following year he was ready to try again, and this time Field was crowned with success. Not a single incident marred the laying. Furthermore, with grappling hooks, the last cable was found, raised, and spliced. Now Field's company could send transatlantic messages from New York and London at the same time.

In 1860, one didn't go to a Western Union office to wire, "CONGRATULATIONS MOM AND DAD ON YOUR SILVER WEDDING ANNIVERSARY," or "SUSIE ARRIVED THIS MORNING SEVEN POUNDS GRACE DOING FINE." Telegraph messages were expensive even by modern standards, and the telegraph companies were used mainly by the news agencies, big business, and government. The Associated Press, organized in 1848, was the best customer. The New York Stock Exchange was also an important source of revenue.

By 1861, there were three great telegraph systems: Western Union, the American Telegraph Company, and the Washington & New Orleans Telegraph Company. As a result of successive mergers, only Western Union remains today. In addition to these, all railroads maintained their own telegraph systems. They were used to relay orders from station to station. Among the railroad telegraph operators were some of the most expert senders and receivers. At the outbreak of the Civil War, thirty operators were selected from the Pennsylvania Railroad to staff the first military telegraph system.

One of the problems of the 1861 telegraph operator was that he couldn't leave his set. If he stepped out for a cup of coffee, the most important message of the day might come over the wire. If a railroad telegraph operator left his set, it might be clicking out: "STOP NO. SEVEN. BRIDGE OUT THREE MILES WEST OF HARTORD."

Then someone came up with an idea. A short pencil was attached to the bar atop the electromagnet which moved up and down, clicking out the dots and dashes. Under the pencil, a roll of paper was placed which was controlled by a steel spring. Now the operator could leave the room, and if a message came in while he was gone, the pencil jotted the dots and dashes on the roll of paper. It was all there when the operator came back.

For a moment, let's step into the city room of a metropolitan newspaper back in 1862. At the far end of the room, the bearded editor sits at his rolltop desk. A gas light is burning over his head since it is a dark December day. In the center of the room, the reporters sit at long tables, writing their copy in longhand. At the other end of the room is a long table bearing six telegraph instruments. The operators are in their shirtsleeves, wearing green eye shades. All six instruments are clicking at once. The operators take down the news bulletins coming in from the Associated Press and decode them. Even for the most expert, this takes some time. One of the operators takes his decoded bulletin over to the editor and lays it on his desk. "Looks mighty bad at Fredericksburg," he says.

Now let's step into today's daily newspaper office. There is one long, continuous table in the shape of a horseshoe. All around the table are reporters working at their typewriters. Most are using the two-finger, hunt-and-pick system, but are typing rapidly. At the bottom of the horseshoe sits the city editor. He is answering the telephone, handing out assignments to the reporters, and checking their copy. At the end of the room are two machines. They rest on cases and appear to be type-writers without keys. Through a slot in each case there emerges a continuous ribbon of letter-width paper. These machines are *teletypes*.

The machines bang away, and no one seems to pay any attention to them. Finally a reporter gets up and goes to the water cooler. On his return he reaches into the wastebasket and tears off six feet of the 8½-inch-wide tape. This he leisurely lays in front of the editor. The editor tears off two feet of the tape, hands it to the reporter, and says, "Do a half-column rewrite on this, and get some local angles."

Our next visit is to the local United Press International (UPI) bureau which is housed in a cubbyhole on the top floor of the newspaper building. Here we find only one young man, with a harassed look. Within reach of his desk are two teletype machines. One is like that which we saw in the newspaper office. The other has what looks like a typewriter keyboard. One is a receiver, and the one with the keyboard is a transmitter. The young man is typing furiously at his desk, while the receiving teletype is spewing out tape. He finishes his story which has been interrupted by frequent telephone calls from "stringers" (news-spotters throughout the state). He goes to the teletype with the keyboard and types his story. A receiving teletype in the New York City UPI bureau is typing it. Now he tears off the accumulated tape in the waste basket, looks it over, and circles certain bulletins. He throws the "state switch" on the sending teletype, and starts typing the circled items. Every newspaper in the state which subscribes to UPI service is getting the stories simultaneously on teletype.

The principle of the teletype is nothing miraculous. Electromagnets pull down the "typewriter" keys instead of clicking the steel bar of the Morse instrument. When the sender pushes down a key on his keyboard, he simply establishes a circuit with a series of receiving teletypes. All that was needed to make the teletype possible was the invention of the typewriter and a cable which could carry enough circuits to send some fifty messages (letters of the alphabet) at once. Before his death, Morse had developed a cable which could carry four, and that was soon improved upon.

Teletype also serves radio stations with news. Political organizations rent the machines during election campaigns to keep a close watch of trends. Stock market reports are sent over teletype, and if you are rich enough, you could have one installed in your home.

Now, back to the newspaper city room. It is November 7, 1960. This time, most of the reporters are gathered around the teletype. The city editor is reading proof on the first edition, blue-penciling frequently. The teletype is silent for a few minutes, and then starts clattering at top speed. The reporters bend over and scan each word as it types. Suddenly one yells out, "Hey, Boss, stop the presses. Kennedy is in."

It could be argued that Morse's telegraph was the most dramatic breakthrough in the history of communications. Even the telephone, the radio telephone, closed circuit television, and Telstar have not supplanted it. Businessmen, proud parents, newspapers, stock exchanges, race tracks, and radio stations still use it. Until Morse promoted the potentials of his telegraph, communication from the primitive jungle drum to the stage coach had not noticeably accelerated.

Whether Samuel Morse stole or borrowed his knowledge of the electromagnet is beside the point. The fact that he exploited its possibilities, and opened the way for rapid communication to any point where wires could be strung or submarine cable laid, provided the challenge for Alexander Graham Bell to go one step further. And that we find in the next chapter.

6

MR. WATSON, COME HERE

IN MARCH, 1875, JOSEPH HENRY, THE MAN WHO HAD helped an ungrateful Samuel Morse with his telegraph, was sitting in his office at the Smithsonian Institution where he was now the director. A young Scotsman entered and introduced himself as Alexander Graham Bell. He had with him an electrical gadget on which he wanted a patent. He called his apparatus a "phonautograph." Its purpose was to help correct the speech defects of deaf children. A box contained an electromagnet and a diaphragm. A pencil was attached to the diaphragm. When the deaf child spoke into a horn attached to the box, the pencil recorded on a sheet of paper the speech vibrations, much as a modern oscilloscope shows them on a picture tube. Then Bell recorded the same sentence spoken by the child, and the pupil could see the difference and correct his own speech, so Bell said.

The gadget had no use beyond speech therapy, as far as its inventor was concerned, but Joseph Henry saw in it the germ of an idea, which if developed, might make it possible to transmit the sound of the human voice. Henry told young Bell that he "had something there," and that he should work it out to a successful conclusion. Bell confessed that he felt unable to do so because he had insufficient knowledge of electricity. Joseph Henry, who had had his unhappy experience with Samuel Morse, snapped, "Go and get it."

Alexander Graham Bell, who preferred to be called Graham, came logically to his interest in transmitting the human voice. He had been born and educated in Edinburgh, Scotland, and had taught speech in the London schools. Suffering from tuberculosis, Bell came to America. He settled in Boston where he conducted a school for deaf-mutes which was successful enough to win Bell a nation-wide recognition in his field.

Among Bell's pupils was the five-year-old son of George Sanders, a moderately wealthy young man. Sanders became interested in Bell's "phonautograph" and his further electrical experiments. Soon he enlisted the financial backing of a Boston banker, Gardner Hubbard. Not a true scientist, Bell's early experiments were of a hit-or-miss variety.

Bell's immediate interest was in an apparatus which would enable those of his pupils who were not totally deaf to hear his voice. Hubbard and Sanders, more far-sighted than Bell, saw in the latter's experiments the possibility of a new form of public communication which could make them all wealthy. They realized that Bell needed technical advice, and they advanced funds to hire Thomas Watson as an assistant. Watson had worked in an electrical shop which had built models for a number of inventors.

Up to this point, Bell's problems had seemed to him insurmountable. As in the "phonautograph," Bell chose the electromagnet and a diaphragm as the basic elements in his attempts to transmit the human voice. He now found that his most difficult problem was in controlling the variation in the electric current as it transmitted the vibrations of the diaphragm. He could get nothing but a buzz or a squawk to go over the wire. The receiver seemed to work better than the transmitter. Bell's other problem was the best material to use for a diaphragm. He had tried clock springs, strips of metal, and even the eardrum of a human corpse.

Now with Thomas Watson's technical assistance, and after many false starts, the two experimenters found that they were able to transmit electrically the vibrations of a watch spring by thumping it with their fingers. It came, like many discoveries, by accident. As Watson described it: "I plucked it (the spring) to start again. When it didn't start, I kept plucking. Then I suddenly heard a shout from Bell in the next room, 'What did you do? Don't change anything. Let me see!' "

The make-and-break points of the spring had become welded together. The spring had become magnetized and was generating a current of electricity. Ten months later, March 10, 1876, Graham Bell was working in his laboratory, and Watson was in a room two stories above, with his receiver. The circuit was open when Bell, working on a storage battery, spilled acid on his trousers. He yelled to Watson, "Mr. Watson, please come here. I want you." Watson came flying down the stairs crying, "I can hear you, and I heard your words *through the receiver!*"

Had Graham Bell known that his cry for aid to his trousers was the first telephone message in history, he probably would have hesitated and tried to compose something as awesome as Morse's "WHAT HATH GOD WROUGHT?"

Strangely, the first use of the telephone was as a burglar alarm. In 1876, the first subscribers to Bell's telephones were six Boston banks. In each were installed two transmitters connected with the E. T. Holmes Private Detective Agency. The transmitters were left open at night. True, with the sensitivity of Bell's transmitters, a burglar would have had to kick over a waste basket to have been heard, but there was more protection for the banks than ever before.

Sixteen months after Graham Bell burned his trousers with acid, there were 778 telephones in use, all in Boston, although a New Haven exchange was soon to open. There was no need for a telephone directory or numbers. Most of the lines were private: between two banks, a stock broker and a bank, or between the hotels and the railroad station. If you had to call the telephone exchange, you just said, "Hey, Central, get me lawyer Perkins at the Adams House."

In 1877, after the telephone exchanges in Boston and New Haven had proven successful, Gardner Hubbard and A. G. Bell ran their first advertisement:

> The proprietors of the telephone, the invention of Alexander Graham Bell . . . are now prepared to furnish telephones for the transmission of articulate speech through instruments not more than twenty miles apart. Conversation can easily be carried on after slight practice and with the occasional repetition of a word or sentence. On first listening to the telephone, though the sound is perfectly audible, the articulation seems to be indistinct, but after a few trials the ear becomes accustomed to the peculiar sound and finds little difficulty in understanding the words.
>
> The telephone should be set in a quiet place where there is no noise which would intercept ordinary conversation.
>
> Any person within ordinary hearing distance can hear the voice calling through the telephone. If a louder call is required one can be furnished for $5.

A photograph of New York City's Wall Street the morning after the great blizzard of 1888 shows a mass of telephone wires strung on unsightly poles. Although half of the wires have been broken by freezing snow and are lying on the ground, those that remain almost blot out the view of the buildings. This situation grew worse in every American city until firemen couldn't reach a fire where ladders were needed without first cutting the telephone wires. Sleet storms raised havoc wtih telephone communications.

Today we know that this problem has been solved by underground or overhead cables carrying bundles of tiny insulated wires. But the cables have to carry more than this. Gradually the number of telephone circuits in use outgrew the capacity of the cable. There was a limit to how many wires it could carry. In order to keep up with this demand for more circuits, the Bell System, as it was now called, had to find a way of putting more than one circuit on a wire, just as Sam Morse had done with his telegraph. But it couldn't be done the same way.

Now the Bell engineers experimented with using varied frequencies for different circuits on one wire. The experiments were successful. Two or more circuits, they found, could go over the same wire without interference.

We would like to describe the "old-time telephone operator," were not so many of them still at their switchboards that such a label would arouse a nation-wide wave of wrath. Yes, there are still places where you can pick up your phone and ask for the time of day, or where the fire engines are racing to. You can ask your favorite operator how Mrs. Jones is doing at the hospital, or whether Mrs. Brody has had her baby yet.

Before radio, we depended far more upon the telephone operator than we do today. The rules weren't so strict then. We could lift the receiver off the hook of the old wall phone and find out who won the world's heavyweight title that night, the World Series score for the day, the results of the Notre Dame-Ohio game, or the election returns. Of course, the operators were not supposed to be pinch-hitting for the Associated Press, but they did just the same.

Those were "the good old days," but like the steam fire engine, with its gleaming brass and its three white horses, manual telephone switchboards with long rows of operators connecting mazes of circuits couldn't keep up with the times and the public demands for better service. For once, automation was necessary to cope with a labor shortage. There just weren't enough qualified, competent operators around, and not enough could be trained to service the rapidly increasing number of tele- phones. A high-school graduate couldn't be trained over- night to route a long-distance call from Philadelphia to Scottsdale, Arizona. A town of 3,000 people might re- quire twenty full-time operators. So the Bell engineers went to work on dialing.

If you should be permitted to visit a dial central office without a guide, which you won't be, you would find yourself in the midst of electronic mystery. There is not a human being in the exchange office unless he is a main- tenance man. The room is clicking and buzzing with automation. On row after row of upright rods, small cylinders are zooming up and down, making contact with other cylinders. These are finding and making cir- cuits, and obeying the forefingers twirling dials in homes and offices. One calls the police station. Another places a call from Oswego, New York, to St. Augustine, Florida without going through a single long-distance operator.

As with most electrical or electronic means of communications since Sam Morse's telegraph, the dial-switching system is based on electromagnets. It is very simple in principle, but very complex in operation. There are nine positions on your telephone dial (not counting Operator). Now, if there were only nine telephone subscribers in your community, all you would have to do would be to dial 4, for example. When you turned the dial to 4 and released it, an electromagnet in the central exchange would turn to the 4 circuit, and you would have your connection. However, if there were eighteen local subscribers, you would have to dial two digits or letters to get your connection. But suppose there were one hundred telephones listed in your directory. Now the electromagnet operates ten switches, each having ten telephone circuits attached to it. The first number you dialed, say 24, would make contact with the proper switch, and the second number, 167, would connect you with the proper telephone on the 24 switch. Now, by adding more rows of switches, 1,000 telephones could be reached by dialing additional numbers. Each time a row of switches is added, the number of telephones which can be called is multiplied by ten.

The dial system was first used experimentally in 1919. But by 1930, when telephone traffic became too heavy for the step-by-step system which we have just described, the Bell Laboratories developed their Crossbar System. Crossbar is likened to a railroad dispatcher sitting in his control tower, guiding railroad freight cars through a complicated maze of tracks in a large railroad yard.

Crossbar scans a switchboard, finds the circuits not in use, and routes your call through the best and most available circuit. It does this not only in large cities, but it also routes long-distance calls. Crossbar has made it possible for a telephone subscriber in Baltimore to dial a number in Butte, Montana without talking to a single long-distance operator.

From the day Graham Bell called Mr. Watson in another room, the telephone has been powered by storage batteries. Generators, powered by public utility companies, keep them charged. But there are always emergency gasoline generators present in case the power should fail in a great storm. Direct current from the batteries carries the message to your telephone receiver, but alternating current rings the bell which calls you to the phone.

The year 1954 saw the invention of a new telephone battery to power transmission lines, so simple in principle that it seems strange no one thought of it before. In that year, two physicists and a chemist, G. L. Pearson, D. M. Chapin, and C. S. Fuller invented the solar battery.

In the 1930's it had been found that silicon exposed to a bright light would produce voltage. Specially treated silicons produced better results. Further experiments with improved silicons produced a battery with an efficiency of 11 per cent, equal to the very best steam or gasoline engines. This led to experiments with a new kind of battery powered by sunlight. The Bell engineers used the battery to power a rural telephone line in Americus, Georgia. Tests have demonstrated that the solar battery not only powers the line successfully by day, but produces enough surplus electricity to power the line on cloudy days and at night.

Following the lead of the pioneer Cyrus Field, the first transatlantic telephone cable was laid in 1956, a century after Field's victory over distance. The third Bell System cable was laid in 1963. But well before this cable had been laid, it was obvious that additional cables could not meet the demand for intercontinental communication. There were five million overseas calls in 1962. Space, not cables, could be the only answer to transatlantic telephone service. The Bell system had half of the answer already.

Since 1946, in many areas telephone calls had been transmitted by *microwave radio*. A microwave is about as long as a cigarette, and billions of these waves pass a given point every second. This method has many advantages over long-distance telephone cables. It can transmit 11,000 telephone conversations, or six television channels at once. Microwave requires very little power. However, it has its limitations. Unlike conventional radio beams which follow the curvature of the earth's surface, microwave travels from horizon to horizon. In a mountainous area, microwave relay stations send telephone conversations from peak to peak. On the prairies, high towers are required to extend the horizon.

With microwave, the Bell Laboratories have half of

the answer to transatlantic communication through space, but their engineers must wait for the National Aeronautics and Space Administration to provide the other half.

Graham Bell and his telephone had a deep effect on the life of the community, the state, and the nation. It brought the policeman, the fire company, and the doctor within the turn of a crank. The governor could now call out the National Guard in any part of the state by going to his wall telephone. The President of the United States could talk to the governor of a state, man to man, rather than by picking up his pen and writing "Honored Sir." Lawyers found their cases involving "verbal contracts" greatly increased by telephone conversations among businessmen, and farmers' wives found the party line a greater source of gossip than the local weekly newspaper. Yes, Graham Bell's telephone brought everyone *closer together.*

7

MARCONI'S DIT-DIT-DIT

IT WAS AN APRIL NIGHT IN 1899 AND THE SKY SEEMED clear. The skipper of the *R. F. Matthews* wasn't paying much attention to his compass. He knew every inch of this section of the English coast, and he could almost sail it with his eyes closed — in clear weather. But suddenly the *R. F. Matthews* ran into a fog bank, and the skipper wished that he had depended on the compass. He was hopelessly lost.

About a mile away, the Goodwin Sands lightship was

tossing in the English Channel chop. Except for two men on watch, the crew was asleep. It was not until the prow of the *R. F. Matthews* loomed over the lightship's deck that one of the watch was able to give the alarm. The lightship, with no time to weigh her two anchors, was a sitting duck, and the freighter had no time to swerve from its uncertain course. Next, the prow of the *R. F. Matthews* was gashing the iron plates of the lightship's hull, at the same time tearing a hole in her own. As soon as the engines could be reversed, the freighter backed away, but now both ships were leaking badly, and slowly sinking.

In a little shack on the lightship's deck, a man sat at what looked like a telegraph key, and he repeatedly tapped out - . - .   - - . -   - . .   —CQD (SOS was not then the international distress signal). An hour and a half later, when the deck of the lightship was nearly awash and the prow of the freighter was already under water, a fleet of skiffs appeared out of the fog. Everyone on the lightship and the *R. F. Matthews* was saved. For the first time in history, the crews of two ships owed their lives to Guglielmo Marconi and his wireless telegraph.

Guglielmo Marconi's (if you can't pronounce Guglielmo, call him William) first experiment with ether waves was shortly before the *R. F. Matthews* collision. It took place in the luxurious rose garden of Marconi's rich banker-father. Marconi sat at a table . bearing a strange-looking instrument which consisted of a wire coil with a spark gap attached by wire to a Morse telegraph key. A mile away, a friend of Marconi's sat at a similar instrument. From both instruments one wire ran to the top of a tall pole, and another into the ground. There was no wire connecting the two instruments. When Marconi touched his telegraph key, a spark leaped across the gap in the wire coil, and his "signal" traveled to the extended wire of the other "set." There the wire carried the signal down and into a tube filled with nickel and silver filings. The filings, upon receiving the electric impulse sent through the ether, arranged themselves into an excellent conductor, and Marconi's message was carried to a Morse "inker." The "inker" was a later improvement upon the pencil and roll of paper which a lazy telegrapher had earlier attached to the conventional Morse receiver. When Marconi's friend tore the message from his receiver, wireless telegraphy was a reality.

Guglielmo Marconi was born in Bologna, Italy, April 25, 1874. As a boy, ill health required him to get most of his education at home. For this frail lad, science took the place of sports, and his wealthy father bought him a fine technical library. For some time, Marconi's idol was Benjamin Franklin. A bit fearful of repeating Franklin's experiment with the kite and the key in a thunderstorm, Marconi erected an aerial on the roof of his father's house and collected enough static electricity to ring a bell on the first floor.

At a health resort in Switzerland, Marconi read in a magazine about a German scientist who had sent an electric spark across a room. The article set Marconi's brain on fire. If you can send sparks across a room, why not electric impulses across the Atlantic, he thought. This was the turning point in Marconi's life. He now had a single goal. He would invent a new and revolutionary means of world-wide communication, with his messages traveling at the speed of light (186,000 miles per second).

Marconi now focused all his mental power on studying the passage of electricity through the "ether." The theory that electricity travels through the "ether" at the speed of light was first announced by a Scottish scientist, James Clerk Maxwell, known by his students as "Dafty" Maxwell.

Maxwell's "ether" theory sounded plausible when he explained it, but he was never able to prove it. In the 1890's a German scientist, Heinrich Hertz, thought he had proved Maxwell's theory — but today we know that he didn't. Nevertheless, this theory became the basis for experimentation in wireless telegraphy for at least fifteen years. Accepting Maxwell's theory, Marconi went to work and read every word that Hertz had written. Marconi's experiments, based on the writings of Maxwell and Hertz, resulted in victory when he was finally able to send his wireless message a mile. Now he was "thinking big." But the fulfillment of his thoughts required more money than the elder Marconi had, and more capital than could be raised in Italy. In 1896, therefore, the year after his first spectacular experiment, Marconi moved to England, which was then the money capital of the world.

In England, Marconi's first move was to conduct a series of demonstrations before the director of the British Post Office. Why Marconi chose to impress this official is not clear. This method of sending messages certainly would not have increased the sale of postage stamps, and we remember that the U.S. Postmaster General feared Morse's telegraph as he feared a change in administration. But the British Post Office was impressed, and Marconi filed a British patent for what he called "signaling through space without wires."

Lloyd's of London, that great institution which will insure anything from a pianist's hands to the weather at a county fair, launched Marconi on his way to fame and fortune. By 1897, Marconi had succeeded in sending Morse code messages to ships twelve miles at sea. The bulk of Lloyd's business always had been, and still is, insuring ships and their cargoes. From Lloyd's founding up to the time of Marconi's wireless, the company had never known if and when an insured shiip would return. Some were never heard from, and Lloyd's never knew what had happened to them. Owners could sell their ships in foreign ports, claim they were wrecked, and collect the insurance.

Marconi couldn't solve all of Lloyd's problems, but he did set up a wireless station on the North Irish coast which could send Lloyd's reports of ship arrivals from that point. With the help of Lloyd's and their bankers, Marconi was now able to found the Wireless Telegraph and Signal Company.

But even with this success, Marconi's goal was the same as that day in Switzerland when he had read of the scientist who had sent a spark across a room. "If across a room, why not the Atlantic?" With the incident of the *R. F. Matthews* behind him, Marconi was now a hero, and raising capital for greater experiments presented no problem.

In 1901, Marconi's engineers built a ring of twenty masts for transatlantic transmission. They were no more than completed when a violent storm wrecked all twenty. The engineers were dismayed; but, unperturbed, Marconi's only remark was, "We shall put them up again." While the engineers were rebuilding the wrecked masts, Marconi sailed from England and arrived at St. John's, Newfoundland, on December 6. Since there was no time to build a receiving station on the scale of the transmitter at Poldhu,* Marconi used a large kite with a wire attached for an antenna.

On December 12, the word at both Poldhu and St. John's would have been "Go O.K.," had it been today. In Poldu, Marconi had a dynamo generating 20,000 volts. For no good reason that is apparent, the sending key was three feet long.

The atmosphere was tense in the wireless shack at St. John's. Fortunately there was a good wind, and Marconi's "antenna kite" went up to 400 feet. The time had come for Poldhu to start sending — but nothing was received at

---

* A promintory in S.W. Cornwall, England, where the station is located.

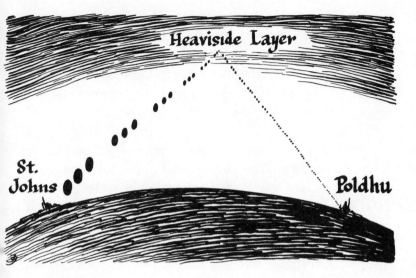

St. John's. The engineers tinkered with the receiving apparatus, but nothing happened. As the sun began to set, Marconi thought something was coming over, but it was garbled, nothing resembling the letter "S" which was to be used for the test. Marconi hadn't learned what radio "hams" quickly learned, in 1920, that for some reason electrical impulses travel through the ether better after dark.

Then finally at 12:30 A.M., on December 13, it came through loud and clear: ... *dit-dit-dit* (S). Marconi had spanned 1,700 miles with the speed of light.

Guglielmo Marconi became an international hero. Americans who couldn't spell Guglielmo named their sons William. But in one sector, Marconi was anything but popular, and that was in the offices of the Anglo-American Cable Company. They were most unhappy that the name of Marconi was eclipsing the fame of their founder, Cyrus Field. They feared the competition of a communication transmission, which used the ether and cost nothing, with the telegraph that sent its messages over a transatlantic cable which had cost $12 million to lay successfully. The Anglo-American Cable Company had purchased exclusive rights to send messages from St. John's, Newfoundland, and they told Marconi to get out — *but fast*.

Marconi, taking these difficult circumstances in his stride, moved his wireless station to Glace Bay, Nova Scotia, and was in business. Marconi's first transmission of dit-dit-dit immediately impressed the world that wireless telegraphy was entirely practical, not only for transatlantic communications, but especially for communication between ships at sea and their home ports. Now a ship could send a wireless message to its owners, and to Lloyd's of London, that it was three days out of Liverpool with a cargo of teakwood. But more important to human lives was the ability of ships to call for help when in distress. Now ambitious young men seeking adventure were spending their evenings at home tapping out CQD on their practice keys, hoping to earn the title "Sparks," which had become the international nickname for ship wireless operators.

On the night of April 14, 1912, the proud new luxury

liner *Titanic* was approaching Newfoundland on her maiden voyage. The huge ship was nearly 900 feet long, had cost $7,500,000, and carried 2,200 passengers and crew. It was a gay evening. Dinner was over, and most of the passengers were dancing to the music of the ship's band, or were strolling in the moonlight. Up in his wireless shack, Sparks was amusing himself by exchanging chatty messages with other ships in the area. Suddenly the searchlights of the great White Star liner picked up the gleaming mass of an iceberg ahead. The officer on the bridge ordered the helmsman to steer sharply to starboard, and signaled the engine room to SLOW. It appeared at first that the *Titanic* would clear the vast white hulk of ice. But at least 75 per cent of an iceberg is under water, and the officer on the bridge could not be sure how much clearance he needed. Then came a jolt and the sound of ripping steel.

It was charged later that the captain should have lowered the lifeboats sooner, and ordered Sparks to send out the CQD immediately. But the *Titanic* was supposed to have water-tight compartments and was theoretically unsinkable. When it was obvious to everyone that the liner was sinking, Sparks began sending CQD frantically. He received replies that several ships in the area were speeding to the aid of the *Titanic*. They arrived too late, and 1,503 lives were lost. When the *Titanic* made its final plunge, the ship's band was on deck playing "Nearer My God to Thee," and Sparks was still sending CQD. The band and Sparks went down with the *Titanic*.

Sparks' CQD had been sent too late, but the *Titanic*'s wireless operator had proved to the world that Marconi's invention could rally aid from all quarters in time of disaster.

Just what had Marconi done? Applying the unproven and erroneous theory of "Dafty" Maxwell, later advanced by Heinrich Hertz, Marconi had made possible the transmission of wireless code messages. He had learned that electric waves can be made to undulate like the surface of a pond when a rock is thrown into it. The length of these waves, he learned, could be controlled just as the waves in the pond could be controlled by throwing a boulder or a pebble in. Marconi's original *wave lengths* were fifteen miles apart for transatlantic signals. It is now estimated that a microwave length of from four to six inches could reach planets outside the Milky Way.

Had Marconi been asked to explain "ether," he would have had difficulty in answering. But by 1913, the wireless telegraph was firmly established as a means of international communication. Now all that was needed for further progress was for someone to do for the wireless telegraph what Alexander Graham Bell had done for Sam Morse's telegraph, much to the latter's irritation.

8

RADIO

IT WAS 9 P.M. ON THE NIGHT OF NOVEMBER 2, 1920. A voice came over the crackling and hissing of the earphones: "We have just received a telegram from Ward 11 in Manchester, New Hampshire. The final vote there is James M. Cox, Democrat — 310, and Warren G. Harding, Republican — 108. However, the total vote in New Hampshire shows Harding in the lead, nearly four to one. You are listening to radio station KDKA in Pittsburgh." Radio had carried the Presidential election returns for the first time in history.

That election night, a handful of people in Pittsburgh heard the returns on the first commercially available radio sets, sold by a local department store for the great occasion. The rest of the radio audience was composed of "hams" who listened on home-made radio sets whose coils were wound around Quaker Oats cartons.

While Alexander Graham Bell required only two and a half years after his first visit to Joseph Henry to establish a commercial telephone exchange, there was a development period of twenty years between Reginald Fessenden's first successful transmission by radio of a voice fifty miles away to the 1920 KDKA broadcast of the election returns.

Lee DeForest is popularly hailed as the patron saint of radio, and rightly so, but the first man to transmit the human voice by radio was a young Canadian, Reginald A. Fessenden. At Bishop's College, Lennoxville, Quebec, Fessenden was not planning a scientific career. But he became fascinated by the works of "Dafty" Maxwell and Hertz. He read of Graham Bell's experiments, and by the time Marconi was sending his code messages twenty miles, Fessenden was professor of electrical engineering at Western University in Pittsburgh.

After graduation from Bishop's College at the age of twenty, Reginald Fessenden was determined to get a scientific education, first from practical groundwork in the laboratory, and second from books. His first step was to get a job in Thomas Edison's laboratory at Llewellyn Park, New Jersey. By day, he acquired a thorough grounding in laboratory practice, and at night he "hit the books." All of his study was focused on sending the human voice through the ether waves. He believed that this could be done if alternating current of 100,000 oscillations per second could be generated. Fessenden's problem lay in the fact that at the time no generator had ever been built which would produce more than 5,000 oscillations per second.

Fessenden might have received some aid in developing a better alternating current generator from his boss, Thomas Edison, had not Edison been known throughout the electrified world as "Mr. Direct Current."

Edison no doubt believed that direct current was the most efficient form of electric power, but this was not correct. Moreover, the use of direct current was immensely profitable to Edison, and it powered all of Edison's light bulbs, streetcar motors, and the wireless telegraph stations of the Marconi Company. But high voltage direct current could not travel far over wires. In a city electrical system, a direct current generator was needed for nearly every neighborhood. Edison built these generators. When Nikola Tesla, one of Edison's employees, demonstrated that alternating current was superior to direct current for commercial use, Edison promptly fired him, and started a publicity campaign to combat him. Edison's most effective piece of propaganda was a picture of a man being electrocuted in the death chamber of a prison. Under the picture was a caption reading, "This is alternating current. Do you want it in your home?"

Now Fessenden began drafting plans for an alternating current generator which he believed could produce vibrations fast enough to send his voice through the ether. While working unsuccessfully on this project, he turned his attention to a receiver which he called a "liquid barreter." This primitive forerunner of the audio tube was a glass bulb containing a wire which ran into a solution of nitric acid. It worked — almost. Fessenden was able to pick up occasional voice sounds, but they were badly distorted, and scarcely audible over the constant buzzing. However, as unsuccessful as the liquid barreter proved to be, it attracted the attention of the U.S. Weather Bureau, which hired Fessenden as wireless research director and set up an experimental station for him at Cobb Island, Maryland. Now Fessenden was free of Edison, and free to devote his entire time to transmitting the human voice without wires.

With a free hand, and the support of the U.S. Weather Bureau, Fessenden built two fifty-foot masts a mile apart. His power was insufficient, and the liquid barreter was still imperfect; nevertheless in 1900, Fessenden was able to send an oral message from one tower to the other — just five years after Marconi had traversed a mile with his dots and dashes.

The widespread publicity resulting from Fessenden's break-through aroused the interest of private capital. Here was something to compete with Marconi's company, and the National Electric Signaling Company was formed. Its sole objectives were to compete for the wireless business and advance wireless telephony. None of the directors envisioned Rudy Vallee or Fibber McGee and Molly.

Reginald Fessenden seemed to be approaching his alternating current goal when General Electric built for his company a generator capable of producing 50,000 oscillations per second. In 1906, with only half of the current oscillations Fessenden believed necessary for wireless telephony, the GE generator enabled him to reach ships twelve miles offshore. Now the directors of the Electric Signaling Company were ready for big business in wireless telephony, but before that was to come, imaginative Reginald Fessenden had something else in mind.

It was Christmas Eve, 1906, and the atmosphere in the wireless shacks on the ships off the Atlantic seaboard was anything but festive. The Sparkses were not in a Yuletide mood. Sure, there was a Christmas tree tied to the foremast, but the boys behind the Morse keys were thinking about their kids back home. Then they began getting the Morse signal cq, cq, cq, which always alerted them when a message was coming. They adjusted their earphones and waited, hoping that it would not be a ship in distress. Suddenly the eyes of every Sparks bugged as he heard, instead of a Morse code message, the slow, majestic strains of Handel's "Largo" played on a violin. Then the violinist played "Silent Night, Holy Night." The violinist was Reginald Fessenden, and the first radio broadcast program had taken place. Fessenden repeated his program on New Year's Eve.

But that broadcast was the last of radio programming for the next fourteen years. The investors in the National Electrical Signaling Company were interested in just one thing — to beat Marconi! During the year following Fessenden's New Year's Eve broadcast, wireless telephonic service was established between New York and Washington. But Fessenden's wireless telephone was hardly satisfactory, and his company was making little progress in attracting the commercial communications market. It was, of course, unable to capture Marconi's transatlantic business, and for intracontinental communication, businessmen found Sam Morse's Western Union more dependable. The trouble still lay in the generator.

If you stay up late enough at night to hear a radio station go off the air, you may hear the announcer say, "This station operates on a frequency of 1400 kilocycles by authority of the Federal Communications Commission." He is telling you that the alternating current which sends you the station's signal is oscillating at 1,400,000 times per second. Fessenden's GE generator could sometimes get up to 80,000 vibrations. With no visible prospect of ever building a generator which could produce 100,000 vibrations, Fessenden was obviously at the end of his trail.

Now the scene changes to Talladega, Alabama, where a schoolboy born in Iowa in 1873, a year before Marconi, is getting mighty tired of being called a "damyankee" by his classmates. Lee DeForest's father, a Congregational minister, had moved his family to Talladega when he was made president of a Negro college. The father had hopes that Lee would become a minister, but Lee was more interested in tinkering. At one stage of his youth, he made a steam engine out of a barrel, but his most important product of that period was the invention of a gate which would open automatically while the farmer sat immobile in the buggy seat.

Lee DeForest was ready for Yale at thirteen, and he too had heard of Heinrich Hertz. Lee worked his way through Yale, and then did graduate work in wireless waves. He developed a "responder," which was something like Fessenden's "barreter" and worked better. At the time, there was a disgruntled group of financiers. They saw a future in wireless telephony and wanted to "get in on the ground floor." They were currently frustrated because they were unable to buy into Fessenden's company. DeForest was attracting some attention for his research at the Western Electric laboratories in Chicago. Soon he was called upon by a group of the unhappy capitalists. They put up money to form the DeForest Wireless Company, with DeForest at its head.

Soon, however, DeForest's backers were suffering from the same "Marconi headaches" as the Fessenden organization. Unable to compete successfully with either Marconi or Fessenden, the directors of the DeForest Wireless Company "dumped" their chief and adopted a new invention which was to be the mainstay of radio for the next ten years — the crystal detector.

General H. C. Dunwoody, U.S. Army, had discovered

in 1906 that a wire held over a crystal stone — carborundum or galena — would pick up voice transmission. The end of the wire became a dial attached to the antenna, and the crystal detector was a reality. Radio "hams" were using them up to 1925, and this detector was used in the Dick Tracy wrist radios which were in Christmas stockings as late as 1950. The crystal detector was cheap, and it worked over short distances.

But Lee DeForest, now exiled to a small laboratory of his own, realized that the crystal detector was not the answer if there was to be a future in the transmission of speech without distortion. He focused his research on an English development which had originally begun in Edison's troubled, unscientific mind.

Thomas Edison was not a scientist, but he was the master "tinkerer" in the history of American invention. His electric light bulb, nearly ready for installation on streets and in houses, was still giving him trouble. Some unidentified current was being generated by the lamp filaments which darkened one side of the bulb. Following his characteristic trial-and-error approach to a problem, he placed a small metal plate in the bulb. Edison became convinced that some kind of current was leaping from the filament to the plate, but he couldn't explain it. Later, trained scientists looked into the problem and theorized that the "current" was a stream of electrons thrown out by the filament onto the plate.

At this point, an English scientist named Fleming took over. Toying with Edison's experimental light bulb, the metal plate, and the filament, Fleming found that he had a detector tube which picked up radio signals better than the crystal. DeForest obtained some Fleming tubes, tested them, and concluded that Fleming was on the right track but had not developed anything efficient enough for commercial use.

To the Fleming tube, DeForest added a grid between the filament and the plate. Now the electrons passed through the grid to the plate. The grid, attached to the antenna, could control the current of the electrons and thus the volume. But DeForest's most important discovery, one which revolutionized radio transmission, was that his tube, which he called an *audion,* not only

Audion Tube
(de Forest) 1908

Arnold High Vacuum
Tube - 1913

served as the best detector invented thus far, but also could generate high frequency current. In fact, the audion could produce beyond the power of any generator which man could build in 1907, when DeForest patented the audion on January 29. The audion meant billions of dollars in new industry — and thousands of jobs.

It was Dr. Irving Langmuir of General Electric who added the final touch to DeForest's invention. Langmuir found that the audion functioned better in a vacuum. DeForest's audion became the vacuum tube.

With his goal achieved in the audion, and rapidly amassing a fortune, Lee DeForest set his sights on new horizons. He wanted to exploit the possibilities of wireless transmission beyond the commercial wireless telephone. First, he equipped all of the ships in the U.S. Navy with wireless telephones. Then he went to Paris in 1910 for his first "stunt" broadcast. There he broadcast a program to Marseilles, 500 miles away. The top of the Eiffel Tower served both as his studio and his antenna. Returning to New York, he staged a broadcast from the Metropolitan Opera, with the great Caruso singing into a microphone little better than a telephone transmitter.

World War I put a temporary damper on the development of radio. Security precautions put all "hams" off the air. Their "by guess and bigorry" experiments had contributed much to the more scientific work of the engineers. But as early as 1916, young David Sarnoff, an executive of the Marconi Company, was convinced that a "radio music box" could be built in mass production for $75, and that several million sets could be sold within a few years.

After the Armistice of November 11, 1918, President Wilson said that he didn't like to see the British-controlled Marconi Company monopolizing wireless communication, and he encouraged General Electric to organize the Radio Corporation of America. Not to be outdone, Westinghouse organized its own radio division. But in spite of Sarnoff's predictions and DeForest's demonstrations, both companies were thinking only in terms of radio telephony.

Now the "hams" began to carry the ball for radio as a means of public communications. Many "doughboys" and "gobs" came back from the U.S. Signal Corps and the battleships with wireless training. They came back to build their own little transmitters and receivers. Most of them used the old crystal detector and the Quaker Oats coil, but many were using the DeForest audion tubes. These do-it-yourself units were miniature radio stations, right out of *Popular Mechanics*. At first, they talked to and listened to their pals in the next block, exchanging neighborhood gossip. But also they pushed their phonographs up to their transmitters. Occasionally a ham's wife would play the piano for Bill Smith and his wife over on Elm Street.

Not all of the "hams" had the know-how to build transmitters. Many high-school students were satisfied with home-made crystal receiver sets. They listened to the "ham" transmissions, and would call in requests for their favorite phonograph records — "Dardanella" for instance. Soon the "ham" stations were developing audiences and getting fan mail.

In 1919, Dr. Frank Conrad, a physicist doing research for Westinghouse in Pittsburgh, was running a series of tests for improving ship-to-shore telephone service. He had no regular schedule, but was picked up by a considerable number of "hams." They sent him post cards asking that he go on the air at regular intervals so they could get his signal and test the efficiency of their home sets. Dr. Conrad sensed that fan letters from a maximum number of "hams" would greatly enhance the results of his tests. He announced that he would go on the air every Thursday and Saturday evening for one hour. To attract more "ham" listeners than he would draw from repeating, "This is Frank Conrad. How well do you hear me?" he played records, read the major league baseball scores, and his son rounded up his friends for talent shows. The fan mail soon indicated that there was considerable interest in physicist Frank Conrad's bi-weekly programs.

It was the summer of 1920, and for the first time, a Pittsburgh department store offered home radio sets, built by Westinghouse, which would enable more Pittsburgh people to listen to Dr. Conrad and the Pryor's Band playing "The Whistler and His Dog," as well as reassurance that the Pirates were doing fine.

Finally, Westinghouse realized what was happening

— that Dr. Conrad was selling radio sets. The vice-president of Westinghouse called a conference of division heads and they decided to forget about wireless telephony for the time being and focus on the 1920 Presidential election returns, scooping the nation.

As soon as the Republican and Democratic National Conventions had nominated Warren G. Harding and James M. Cox, respectively, preparations were made by Westinghouse to build the first commercial radio station. Its call letters were KDKA. The studio was a shack built on the roof of the Westinghouse factory and there was just room enough for three men to get the telephoned returns from a local newspaper, plus an announcer.

The November 2, 1920, election night broadcast changed the future of wireless transmission. Those without radio sets that night were disappointed, and those who owned them were the envy of their neighbors. Now Westinghouse, which had received nationwide publicity for its election news coverage, had to come through with a follow-up. The public, at least in Pennsylvania, expected KDKA to *produce*.

In 1920, and still today to some extent, large companies subsidized employee concert bands. A company band was considered not only good employee-management relations, but also a status symbol. A Westinghouse band superior to the General Electric band just showed that GE didn't have what it took. And a Colt Revolver band which played better than the Remington band signified that Remington had never learned how to make a good revolver. At least that was what management thought in 1920.

And so the Westinghouse band took to the air to satisfy those who demanded more from KDKA after the election coverage. It was the first musical ensemble of any size to do a live broadcast, and its influence on broadcast production was fundamental. The first band concerts were broadcast from the company's auditorium. And there were complaints of every sort. Listeners wrote that their sets couldn't take the volume; that the band blew out tubes; that the echoes and vibrations of the auditorium spoiled reception.

Unable to think of a better solution, KDKA moved the band broadcasts to the roof of the factory. Reception was reported to be better. But sometimes it rained, and Westinghouse put up a tent for the band. This was better still, according to the radio fans. Then one night, just before a broadcast, a high wind blew the tent down. In a hurry, the tent was taken into the factory and erected in a large assembly room. The fans said this was "the best yet."

So Westinghouse had the answer for the first all-purpose radio studio. It set aside a room for broadcasting and lined the walls with burlap. A heavy carpet lined the floor. The carbon "mikes" no longer shattered, and Westinghouse radios began selling like hot cakes.

Westinghouse's next "first" was what we call today "remote control." It began broadcasting services from Pittsburgh's Calvary Episcopal Church. This was a production feat for the day. Three microphones picked up the organ, the rector, and the choir. There was no control panel in the modern sense. The engineer simply threw switches to the "mike" located in front of the center where the service was being conducted.

With the mounting fan mail from broadcasts of the band, sports results, and the Calvary Episcopal Church, KDKA and Westinghouse were convinced that the future of radio for public communications and entertainment was assured. In 1921, Westinghouse opened WJZ in Newark, New Jersey, and WBZ in Boston. Temporarily left behind, RCA now plunged into the mainstream of radio, and put WDY, New York City, on the air. WDY's first triumph was in carrying the Dempsey-Carpentier heavyweight championship fight on July 2, 1921. In October they further challenged Westinghouse by carrying the World Series.

Up to this point, the radio set and the loudspeaker had not been wedded. Families huddled around their radio set, taking turns at putting on the earphones. Children fought over whose turn was next. Although Westinghouse now owned three radio stations, none of its engineers had thought of connecting them with a telephonic hookup.

But electrical amplification of public events had already taken place. It is probable that its first spectacular use was during a Republican rally at the Minnesota State Fair in September, 1920, where four "horns" carried the voice of Presidential candidate Warren G. Harding.

The photograph of the rally shows the loudspeakers looking like old-fashioned phonograph horns. The first makeshift speakers for home radio sets were simply metal horns attached to earphones.

President Harding was the participant in another radio "first." On November 11, 1921, just a month after WDY had first carried the World Series, Harding delivered his Armistice Day address into a microphone at Arlington National Cemetery. His voice was carried over telephone wires to New York and San Francisco. He was heard by a crowd of 35,000 in New York's Madison Square Garden, and 20,000 in the San Francisco Plaza. The two vast gatherings joined with those at Arlington Cemetery in singing hymns. Now Westinghouse and RCA saw the light.

Radio had never used telephone lines except for local remote-control broadcasts. Impressed by the Harding hookup, station WEAF, New York, was linked by telephone to Stagg Field in Chicago, from which it broadcast the Princeton-Chicago football game on October 28, 1922. Then on January 4, 1923, WNAC in Boston was joined to WEAF by telephone.

These first "network" broadcasts were poor in quality, since conventional telephone lines were not built to carry fine music. But the Bell System saw the potential revenue from network broadcasting, and immediately developed lines especially designed for radio transmission. In 1924, twenty stations carried a major speech by President Calvin Coolidge. However, networks were improvised only for very special occasions — sports events, inaugurals, the President lighting the White House Christmas tree, and the like.

The mushrooming radio industry now faced two forms of growing pains, and the first was *interference*. Most local stations were operating on approximately the same wave lengths, 360 to 400 meters. Thus, radio stations in neighboring cities often "jammed" each other. The temporary solution to the problem seemed to be for these stations to share time, one station taking the air from 7 A.M. to 6 P.M., then relinquishing the wave length to its neighbor. But although the term "prime time" had not been invented, station managers grumbled. Most businessmen resent government regulation, but most radio-station managers were not unhappy when the embryo Federal Communications Commission stepped in and assigned 110 radio channels.

It is difficult to understand how the second problem of radio production in the 1920's, the cost, could not have been anticipated. In confronting this problem, the radio tycoons seem to have ignored their brothers in communications, the newspaper publishers. Back in 1920, Westinghouse had believed that occasional talks by Frank Conrad would sell radios, and so they did. But by 1922, the entertainment and informational appetite of the radio audience was insatiable. It demanded radio programs from dawn to midnight. At first, entertainers, both amateur and professional, looked upon a radio performance as fun and a new experience. College professors welcomed a chance to offer their knowledge free, via radio. But soon the supply of free talent was exhausted. Studio orchestras and organists had to be hired. Radio manufacturers who had built stations to sell their products now found that too large a share of their profits was going into operating these stations.

Then someone at WEAF, New York, had a bright idea. In 1922, a group of promoters were selling lots in a Long Island real estate development. WEAF offered them five ten-minute programs for $500. The "commercial" had come to stay.

The need for support of good radio programs demanded advertising from the producers of nationally distributed products, and the only way such accounts could be obtained was by promising sponsors wide coverage. For this, network broadcasting was absolutely basic. And so they came: RCA's National Broadcasting Company on November 15, 1926, with an inaugural broadcast featuring symphony orchestras, Mary Garden from the Metropolitan Opera, famous dance bands, and humorist Will Rogers. By the summer of 1927, NBC was operating two networks, the Red and the Blue, with a combined forty-eight stations. This was by no means national coverage, but it provided for coast-to-coast broadcasting, and one could hear a description of the Rose Bowl game in New York. In 1929, William S. Paley launched the Columbia Broadcasting System at about the same time Mutual took to the air.

Now the floodgates were open for large-scale network advertising by nationally known products. Each had its own program format and features — *The A & P Gypsies* with a good concert orchestra, *The Happy Wonder Bakers* for General Mills; *The Eveready Flashlight Hour* with thirty minutes of light concert music; *The Cities Service Band*; *The Dutch Masters Minstrels*; and *The Lucky Strike Hour*. But better still, the New York Philharmonic Orchestra and the Metropolitan Opera were both being heard with commercial sponsorship.

By 1928, radio was an important factor in politics, and politicians were well aware of this. The rasping voice of Al Smith in the 1928 Presidential campaign doubtless cost him votes. Herbert Hoover, who knew he sounded dull on the air, avoided radio whenever possible. The day of the bellowing candidate was over. The carbon "mikes" just wouldn't take it. Thomas E. Dewey, a former choir singer, attracted the attention of political leaders when he reported to the public, via radio, in a rich baritone voice, on his racket-busting as District Attorney for New York County. The "Dewey voice" was an important factor in carrying him to the Governor's Mansion in Albany, and from there to the Republican Presidential nomination. Even without the depression, Herbert Hoover's colorless delivery would have left him far behind the ringing voice of Franklin D. Roosevelt in 1932. From the White House, FDR's cheerful broadcast of Fireside Chats helped speed his legislative program. Until the advent of television, a *radio* personality was the looked-for ingredient in the selection of a candidate for public office.

Although the loudspeaker had become a part of the

radio set, the quality of sound was still far from hi-fi. But at this point, in the latter 1920's, two former rivals, the phonograph and the radio, joined forces. When the first mass-produced radio sets came on the market, the old family phonograph went up into the attic. As poor as radio transmission was, it caught the public fancy. It was a novelty, almost magic; its programs were live with on-the-spot news. There was also an ever-present challenge of how distant a station could be and remain effective as far as reception was concerned. The phonograph companies were virtually out of business. Brunswick, Edison, Aeolian, and numerous other companies disappeared from the market. The public refused to tolerate the old acoustical records which picked up so few low frequencies that tubas had to be substituted for bass viols in recording orchestras.

But now the recording companies borrowed from radio. They discarded the old acoustical horn into which the music had been played and transferred to a wax record by means of a diaphragm with a needle in its center. A microphone now put the music on the record, and Paul Whiteman's orchestra made one of the first electrical recordings, using the *Rapsody in Blue* which George Gershwin had just completed. With the new electric phonograph came speakers with amplifying tubes. The new speakers now became an important factor in radio sets. Radio tone quality improved. All-directional microphones eliminated the need for a dozen "mikes" to pick up a symphony orchestra. And from that day to this,

scientists and sound engineers have been working to
bring us better tone quality.

FM

Even today, your car radio, or any conventional AM
radio, does not work well in a thunderstorm, because
what we call static blots out the voice or the music coming from a radio station. But you can watch your favorite
TV program while the lightning is flashing right over
your head, and there is neither distortion of sound nor of
picture. This is because the sound in your set is transmitted by FM. Also if you own an FM radio, you can
listen without interference from static.

Edwin Armstrong was the father of FM. Born in New
York City, December 18, 1890, Armstrong tinkered with
home-made radio sets as a boy. He was headed for a
career in electrical science. In 1910, Armstrong began
experimenting with DeForest's audion, and made improvements which enabled him to pick up signals from
San Francisco, and even Hawaii — fantastic distances for
those days.

By 1915, Armstrong had turned his attention to static.
He was convinced that radio vibrations and static had
the same frequencies; that a flash of lightning entered
the radio receiver in the same way that speech was received. He saw his problem clearly but hadn't found an
answer.

By 1920, still without an answer, Armstrong was told
by the best minds in radio engineering that he might as

well give up. Static could never be eliminated. All they could do, they said, was to step up the power on the transmitters. But a bolt of lightning could also step up its power, and the annoyance was still present.

Now Armstrong tried another tack. He began experimenting with wave-lengths other than those used by conventional radio. In conventional radio the wave-lengths remains constant. Sound is *impressed* upon it by voltage. This is called *amplitude modulation* — AM. Edwin Armstrong reversed the AM process by varying his wave-lengths while keeping the voltage constant. In 1935, he put on a demonstration of FM by sending a signal from Yonkers, New York, to New York City, a distance of fifteen miles, operating on two and one half meters. The static-free signal was sent with power that wouldn't have pushed an AM signal across the street.

Encouraged by the success of his demonstration, Armstrong built his own experimental FM station at Alpine, New Jersey in 1937, and began broadcasting recorded music. Now it was noticeable that FM not only eliminated static but markedly improved the fidelity of music and speech. If a silver spoon was dropped on the studio floor, it sounded like a silver spoon, not a steel girder. If the studio was supposed to be silent, there was no hissing or "fat-frying" on FM.

Now the owners of the Yankee Network, a New England chain of radio stations, became interested in Armstrong. They invested $200,000 in an experimental FM station forty-five miles from Boston. They persuaded

RCA to build some FM receiving sets for sale in the area. When they appeared in department stores, Boston music lovers snatched them up as fast as they could be put on the counters.

General Electric, which had previously shown no interest in FM, now built two experimental stations, fifteen miles apart, near Schenectady, New York. Here the GE engineers made a discovery, by accident, which further demonstrated the advantages of FM over AM. While driving from one station to the other, they had an FM receiver in their car. At a point on the highway, the station which they had just left faded out. There was a short distance with no reception. Then the station to which they were driving came in on their receiver. There was no overlapping, no interference as there would have been if two AM stations had been broadcasting on the same wave-length within fifteen miles of each other. Back at the laboratories, the engineers' slide rules seemed to tell them that it would be possible for fifty FM stations to broadcast from one city without interference.

By this time, radio manufacturers were enthusiastic about Armstrong's FM. In Chicago, 25,000 sets were sold in a few months. World War II not only halted production but also discouraged the building of transmitters. Today, however, there are few large cities without at least one FM station. They are the stations for listeners who insist on a high degree of fidelity, whether it's jazz, opera, or symphonic music that is being transmitted. But the greatest contribution of Edwin Armstrong's Frequency Modulation is to the sound in your television set.

It is almost impossible to estimate the impact that radio has had on our daily lives — on our culture, politics, and thinking. Television keeps us informed visually, but its advance in communication is nothing compared to what radio accomplished.

Try to imagine an America before 1925, when there was no radio. Few people outside the District of Columbia had ever heard the voice of a President of the United States. The leaders of the world's great powers were far away — we could read their words but their voices were unknown. For music, the small-town resident was limited to the church choir, the movie pianist, the town band, and the phonograph which played 78 rpm records that had only four minutes of music to a side.

All news was controlled by newspaper deadlines, usually 11 P.M. for morning dailies. If a great disaster occured after that, it took twenty-four hours before anyone could read about it. And most people didn't get their papers until thirty-six hours after the event. The news of President Harding's death did not reach this writer's home town until noon on August 3, 1923. He had died the previous afternoon.

The only way the average adult could learn anything about political issues was from his newspaper editorial, the barbershop, and the political rally. Major candidates were seen and heard by only a small group. Political rallies, with their torchlight parades, bands, and fiery speeches were emotional but hardly informative.

Entertainment, especially in small towns, was confined to the movies, the reading of magazines, cards, the circus once a year, backing up the town baseball team, amateur minstrel shows, and running to fires. The housewife could not foresee the day when she would be entertained while doing her ironing.

And then, suddenly, life was changed in America. The voice of the President was in the living room, and it was the same voice that was speaking to Congress that very moment. Yes, the speech could be read in the paper the next day. But the paper couldn't carry the ring of the voice (if there was any), the emphasis, the ad-libbing which was not in the mimeographed copy given the correspondents, and the response of the listening congressmen.

If there was a train wreck in Indiana, the people at home received the news before it reached the newspaper office, and often an announcer gave an on-the-spot description of the removal of the bodies.

The colorful political rally, slowly dying, finally expired with television. Now the folks in the living room heard every major candidate without leaving the house, and with a chance to listen without the cheering, tub-thumping background. In addition, skilled commentators, for the first time, analyzed the issues of the campaigns. On election night, communities no longer had to rely for the returns on local telephone operators or the magic-lantern screen at the town hall.

Entertainment? The radio listener had his choice of

everything the entertainment world had to offer: good bad, or indifferent. People in towns of no more than 1,000 could hear the New York Philharmonic Orchestra and the Metropolitan Opera. Others could enjoy Amos and Andy, Fibber McGee and Molly, or Rudy Vallee and his Connecticut Yankees. Shut-ins could attend church by radio.

The radio served the public in practical ways as well. The farmer received the day's produce prices before taking his potatoes to market. Perhaps after hearing the broadcast he might decide not to sell just yet. If he were getting ready to cut his hay that afternoon, the radio might tell him to wait until after the thunder showers which were on the way. University extension services brought the housewife new recipes. She had been depending on those in the Grange Cookbook for the past twenty years. The fisherman got advice on "where they were biting," as well as hints on tackle. The businessman received the stock market reports twice daily instead of waiting for the morning newspaper.

Yes, there was trash on radio, or that was what some people called it. The soap opera and the doctor series were on the air forty years ago, but no one had to listen if he didn't want to. The great gift of radio was the raising of a great curtain. It brought government, and the nations of the world, into our living room. We could listen and form our own opinions. There was no longer any excuse for the average person not to be *informed*.

9

TELEVISION

THE ADVERTISING MANAGER FOR CARTER'S LITTLE LIVER
Pills in 1877 would have been heartened had he known
that a Frenchman named Senelecq believed that an
image could be transmitted electrically. Senelecq proposed that an electric current be focused on a mosaic of
selenium cells, with each cell connected to a separate
circuit. Nothing practical came of Senelecq's 1877 pro-
posal for television. It might have worked, but it was as
impractical as that early experimental telegraph which

required a circuit for each letter of the alphabet. So for seven years, physicists forgot about sending pictures by electricity.

But in 1884, a German named Paul Nipkow came upon the basic principle of television, the principle upon which television operates today. Nipkow's method was much simpler than Senelecq's. The German scientist proposed that an image be "scanned" through holes in a rotating disc. A single selenium cell would register the amount of light passing through the holes, thus creating a varying circuit. Nipkow's theory made sense to those high in the world of electricity, but since no one had thought of a way to receive the transmitted picture, nothing was done about it. Furthermore, the telephone was in its infancy, and Marconi was only ten years old.

For forty-one years, the attention of electrical scientists was focused on the development of the telephone, wireless telegraphy, and the radio. Then the year 1925 saw the first transmission of pictures *over wires* in both the United States and England. In both countries, Nipkow's rotating disc transmitted and received the pictures over a telephone wire. That same year, V. K. Zworkin, a Russian applied for a patent on the *iconoscope*, the basic television camera. It employed a cathode-ray tube developed by a German, F. Braun, in 1905.

At this point, one might ask, "Why were the scientists and electrical tinkerers of the United States doing little about the electrical transmission of pictures while the engineers in Europe had been experimenting since

1877?" The answer lay in two approaches to invention in that period, on the two sides of the Atlantic. Men such as Senelecq, Nipkow, Zworkin, and Braun were scientists for science's sake. Their work was sponsored by their governments and universities. They did not work for RCA or Bell Laboratories.

On the other hand, when Joseph Henry experimented with the English electromagnet, he was aiming for its practical use which would line his pockets. When Samuel Morse covered the Democratic National Convention of 1844, he was dreaming of Western Union. And when Tom Edison developed the direct current generator and the incandescent lamp, he was thinking of electric power stations all over the world paying royalties to Thomas Alva Edison. The history of American invention has been that of an idea in the mind of an individual, and the development of that idea by private capital. Not until the dawn of nuclear warfare, and Russia's *Sputnik I*, did our government engage in large-scale sponsorship of science.

Now with commercial radio firmly established, the Radio Corporation of America set its sights on joining radio with the transmission of pictures. In 1933, using the iconoscope which still was based on Zworkin's invention, RCA sent pictures and sound from New York to Philadelphia. By 1936, RCA was conducting widespread field tests, and was nearly ready for commercial television when it was stopped by the Federal Communications Commission which wanted to review RCA's standards. By 1941, the FCC was satisfied, and authorized RCA to launch full-scale TV with commercial sponsorship. But again RCA was stymied by Pearl Harbor, and it was not until 1947 that TV home receivers went into mass production.

Thus far we have traced the development of picture *transmission*, so now let's go to the *receiving* end. Two phenomena help make this easily understandable. The first is that, as most of us know, the human eye holds an image for a fraction of a second after the image has vanished. When one moves his head very rapidly from left to right, and back again, the vision is blurred because the eyes are retaining part of the left scene while picking up the scene on the right. The second key to TV reception is demonstrated to you when your set isn't working well.

Behind the screen of your TV set, a little spot of light, traveling back and forth, traces a number of parallel lines. The spot's brightness depends on the energy being sent from the camera into the transmitter. The spot of light in your set traces thirty of these parallel lines per second. Because your eyes retain an image slightly after it has disappeared, the lines which the little spot of light traces merge into a black and white picture. You have seen a clear picture break down into these lines when your TV set is not working properly.

In order to keep away from AM radio wave-lengths, television operates at very high frequency (VHF). These wave-lengths do not follow the curvature of the earth, but like FM radio which is television's sound, travel in a straight line until they hit the horizon. For this reason, the range of a television station is only from seventy-five to one hundred miles if the transmitter antenna is from 250 to 1,000 feet high, and depending on the contour of the terrain over which the station's beam travels. This is the reason why a high mountain makes an ideal location for a transmitter.

You may have picked up TV signals on your home set from greater distances than the above limits. This sometimes happens when the beam of a distant station bounces off mountains, or is reflected by other phenomena. However, the quality of the picture is usually erratic, nearly always foggy, and accompanied by "snow storms."

With this limited range of television transmission, it was possible for the FCC to establish channels from 2 to 13 throughout the country without interference. These VHF channels operate on 54 to 216 megacycles. Recently the FCC authorized the use of ultra high frequency (UHF), opening up a new series of channels from 14 to 83, to operate on 470 to 890 megacycles. This will make possible a vast increase in the number of television stations and a greater variety in programing, since UHF channels do not interfere with VHF reception.

PAY TV

Many people are dissatisfied with the content and quality of the network TV programs. They would prefer more opera and fine plays rather than run-of-the-mill comics or westerns. There are others who would like to watch athletic events during the "prime time." There are still others, who make up the largest TV audience, who are happy with the programs they are getting.

This wide difference in the public taste has led to experiments with "pay TV." In "pay TV," the viewer pays his money and takes his choice. He can choose to watch only opera, drama, athletic events, fine old movies, travel documentaries, or politics. He does not have to sit through commercials because he has paid for the privilege of avoiding them. The "pay TV" viewers pay for the entire cost of operating a TV station at a profit, without advertising.

Naturally, in "pay TV" there have to be safeguards against anyone getting the telecasts who doesn't pay for them, and the best method so far seems to be this: The program is transmitted from the station completely scrambled. No nonpaying TV set owner can pick up anything resembling a picture. The sound is also scrambled into gibberish. The TV fan who wants to subscribe for his favorite type of program buys from his "pay TV" station a small gadget which he attaches to the back of his set. This gadget has a slot for the insertion of a card with a printed circuit on it. This card and its circuit will unscramble the program he has paid for. Each month he buys a card for the program he wishes to watch. By the end of the first month he may have tired of opera, and he buys a card for progressive jazz, or he may buy two cards, so that he may divide his viewing hours between Shakespeare and wrestling. But when he gets a hankering for *Bonanza*, he takes out the card and dials Channel 6.

EDUCATIONAL TV

We have been discussing television as part of the story of communication. But like radio, most commercial television time is devoted to entertainment, not communication. Huntley-Brinkley are a part of communication. Jackie Gleason is not. Commercial television communication includes news commentators, political analysts, documentaries, national party conventions, astronauts in orbit, Presidential telecasts, news of disasters, and so on. Television's greatest role in communication was the near round-the-clock, uninterrupted telecasting of "The Tragic Four Days," from the moment of President Kennedy's assassination to his burial in Arlington National Cemetary.

But the kind of TV which devotes a majority of its time to true communication is *educational TV*. Most of these stations are low in power, thus short in range. They operate on limited budgets, being on the air usually for only part of a day or evening. The funds come from foundation grants, state legislatures, universities, private schools, and from just plain "passing the hat." These stations had their beginning in 1952 when the FCC reserved 254 frequencies for noncommercial use. There were thirty educational TV stations operating in 1960.

Educational TV programs include supplementing classroom teaching, classes for parents of preschool children, gardening, landscaping, science, photography, racial problems, adventure, news analysis, foreign relations, history, and adult education. Educational TV fills a gap for many viewers on evenings when there is nothing on commercial TV which they wish to see.

In the area where this writer lives, Tuesday is what he calls a "bad night" for commercial TV. But on WENH-TV, operated by the University of New Hampshire, he can watch the Tuesday *News and Comment with Louis Lyons*. Now Mr. Lyons is no "twinkly" Brinkley, but he is a professor of journalism, and his analysis of the news in depth is worth the loss of an occasional laugh. Then at 7:30, Elliot Norton, one of the nation's top drama critics, interviews the cast of a play which has opened in Boston before its New York run. By the time Mr. Norton has finished his series, one gets a pretty good idea of the plays he wants to see that season. Next, there is a program on square dancing that would make anyone want to get right out on the barn floor and swing his partner. The rest of the evening is given over to a concert by the Boston Symphony Orchestra.

The most important role of educational TV is not in bringing new interests and hobbies to the adult viewer. Its greatest value is in communicating with the pupils and teachers in the classrooms. There are still a great many elementary schools in the country in which the upper grades are not "departmentalized," where there is one teacher for everything from English and arithmetic to physical education. There are just as many high schools where one person teaches geometry, biology, and chemistry, while another has English, social studies, and world geography. Obviously, these teachers cannot be experts in all of these subjects. But educational TV can give them an "assistant" once or twice a week who is an expert in a subject to which he has devoted years of study. Educational TV can give close-up views of chemistry and physics experiments which can be seen better on the screen than in the classroom. The educational TV "lab" has equipment which many schools cannot afford.

Most educators agree that television will never displace the classroom teacher. At first, it was predicted that in ten years all teaching would be done by educational TV, and the classroom would need someone only to switch channels and act as a "policeman." This prophecy has not come to pass and never will. But educational TV will increasingly become an aid to more effective teaching, adding a stimulating plus to classroom sessions. When the newspaper editor said, "A picture is worth 1,000 words," he was saying something that is as true in the schools as it is in the city room.

Up to now, we have discussed the cause but not the effect of television. This is difficult to assess, as TV has been with most of us for only fifteen years, while we have forty-five years of radio behind us.

In the entertainment field there is certainly more pleasure in *seeing* the show. Whether the material used in television entertainment is any better than the old radio scripts is questionable. TV entertainment has improved on radio by introducing, in some instances, extraordinary talent. Danny Kaye is not only a great comedian, but he has frequently introduced good ballet, scenic design, and costuming. Because his movies required almost constant speech, it was not until television that Red Skelton revealed himself as one of the two greatest mimes in the world (the other "great" is the French Marcel Marceau). With Red's artistry, the cave man would hardly have had to invent language.

Television brings us what words cannot describe: the emotions of a crowd, the desolation of poverty, the grandeur of nature, the curiosity of a little child, the angry flames of a great fire, or the ferocity of a riot. Even more than radio, television gives us an excellent opportunity to form our own opinions. On radio, we hear what the commentator wants us to hear. We hear his comments on TV as well, but as we watch the scene he describes, the picture may reveal another side of the story. The police officer is interviewed after a Harlem teen-age riot. He represents the law, but the picture on the screen also shows the filthy tenements, the garbage-strewn streets, and the ill-clothed youngsters. No announcer could describe adequately the picture of great dignity displayed at the Negro march on Washington, nor could a radio paint a picture of Dr. Martin Luther King's character by only carrying his voice.

For good or for bad, television has had a tremendous emotional impact on people everywhere. The inaugura-

tion of a President makes everyone proud he is an American and renews our faith in democracy, regardless of the President's political party. The pageantry of the funeral rites of Sir Winston Churchill and the tribute paid by Queen Elizabeth must have strengthened the Briton's faith in a constitutional monarchy.

But since television makes us witnesses to the great events in the world it also places upon us a responsibility to judge impartially what we see as well as hear. We must be aware that we can be influenced by the camera and the men behind it. After all, we see only what the camera records. We saw Premier Khrushchev pounding his shoe in the United Nations. We also saw him laughing and joking with Vice-President Nixon. Well, what kind of man is he? We saw Vice-President Nixon in the Great Debates with the late John F. Kennedy. Nixon looked ill-groomed, with a five-o'clock shadow, while Kennedy looked as if he had just stepped out of Brooks Brothers. Could a better camera angle and better lighting been used on Nixon? Did the production man's handling of the situation influence our evaluation of the two candidates?

Will television influence our system of criminal law? There has been one striking instance, and possibly there will be more, when a TV camera happened to be focused on a scene where a crime was unexpectedly committed. Will a film record, seen by millions, permit a fair trial for the accused?

Yes, because of television, the American public is better informed than ever before. But with so much information available from the audio-visual television, we need more than ever before to be discriminating in interpreting what we see and hear. The American of 1835 knew that his newspaper "slanted" the news politically, and he took that into account. The radio listener one hundred years later realized that on certain networks news commentators could not find anything favorable to report about Franklin D. Roosevelt. Now we not only hear what the commentator wants us to hear, but we are also at the mercy of the cameramen.

However, the intelligent newspaper reader of 1835 analyzed what he read in even the most politically biased newspaper. The paper usually printed the facts even though they were printed with a political "slant." Television shows us events as they happen, even though we may see them from perhaps a predetermined camera angle. It is up to us to "read" the picture, listen to the commentator, and let the truth be *communicated* to our minds.

10

TELSTAR

SEVENTEEN-YEAR-OLD RENE BOURGEOIS AND HIS GIRL FRIEND Clarisse were sitting in a Parisian cafe sipping chocolate. At the far end of the cafe was a wide-screen television set. Above it was a clock which showed 7:30 P.M., Paris time. A French announcer introduced the program. There was a moment of silence with no picture, another announcement in English, and then for the first time, Rene and Clarisse saw the Chicago Cubs. From Wrigley Field the picture changed to the Jefferson and Lincoln

COMMUNICATION

Memorials in Washington, and then to the White House. Again the picture jumped across the continent to the Black Hills of South Dakota where the 350-voice Mormon Tabernacle Choir sang under the sixty-foot heads of Presidents Washington, Jefferson, Lincoln, and Theodore Roosevelt, carved in the side of the mountain. This was the evening of July 23, 1962. Telstar I had relayed its first television program from the United States to Europe, and it had done its job well.

On that same July 23, at 3:30 P.M., when it was 7:30 in Paris, a group of teen-agers had their eyes glued to a TV set in a New Jersey snack bar as Big Ben in London boomed the half hour. Then came pictures of streets and night clubs in Paris, and then St. Peter's in Rome. Telstar I had proved that it could receive as well as transmit.

Yes, Telstar I had transmitted and received a good show, but it was not developed primarily for entertainment or education. It had its birth in a greater need for telephonic communication with Europe, and for a greater knowledge of space. Even with more transatlantic cables and the wireless telephone, it was obvious that the booming demand for telephonic communication with Europe would soon exhaust the resources of both. The use of microwave had helped solve the problem of domestic telephone traffic, but as we know, microwave radio, with its billions of cycles per second, cannot follow the curvature of the earth, and it travels in straight lines. While this problem had been solved on land by building towers at short distances to relay the signal, this would obviously be impractical in spanning the Atlantic.

In 1960, the National Aeronautics and Space Administration (NASA) was working on its Project Echo, and the
Bell Telephone Laboratories were avidly interested. Perhaps a satellite could be the answer, the Bell engineers
thought. As early as 1955, Dr. John R. Pierce, a Bell
physicist, had written a paper theorizing that microwave
signals could be "bounced off" a satellite. On August 12,
1960, NASA's balloon satellite, *Echo I*, proved that Dr.
Pierce was right when voices and still pictures were
received and transmitted by it.

Immediately work was begun on Telstar I, but the
undertaking was so complex and costly that neither private enterprise nor government could do it alone. In
July, 1961, NASA and the American Telephone and
Telegraph Company joined hands. AT&T was to build
Telstar, and pay NASA around $3 million for Delta
launch vehicles and tracking services. Bell engineers
would conduct preliminary communications with television, voice, and high-speed data. NASA would provide
AT&T with all of its data on spacecraft information
acquisition, and — here is a new word — *telemetry*. In
the simplest terms, telemetry is reporting back electronically information, especially on radiation in space, in
answer to coded commands. Finally, AT&T would use
its ground stations which were being built at Andover,
Maine, and Holmdel, New Jersey. Immediately, French
and British communications officials, interested in the
possibilities of Telstar, began building ground stations at
Goonhilly Downs, England, and Plumeur Bodou, France.

On the night of July 10, 1962, a new chapter in communications history was written. To the ordinary American it was as dramatic as Sam Morse's first report from the Democratic National Convention of 1844. Fifteen hours after Telstar I had been launched by a Delta rocket, it had orbited the earth fifteen times. Then AT&T board chairman F. R. Kappel, sitting in the Andover, Maine, ground station, talked to Vice-President Johnson in Washington. Again, Sam Morse seems to have been the only communications inventor to think of awe-inspiring words for such an occasion. After greeting the

Vice-President, Kappel heard, "You're coming through nicely," in a Texas drawl. Actually Kappel's words went from Andover to Telstar, back to Andover, and to Washington by telephone line. But Telstar had proved that it could receive and send.

Telstar had demonstrated that it could handle both code and voice. Now for television. Three minutes after the Johnson-Kappel conversation, a picture of a waving American flag was successfully received and transmitted by Telstar. At 7:45 the French ground station received a picture of Vice-President Johnson and other government officials. From Plumeur Bodou came the report that the sound and picture was as clear as if transmitted twenty-five miles away.

With the dramatic transatlantic telecast of July 23, 1962, Telstar I was taken for granted by people in both Europe and North America. So many scientific miracles had taken place in the previous twenty years that this was looked upon as just one more. There would probably be another next week. But NASA and the Bell Laboratories were taking nothing for granted. Something would go wrong sometime, and Telstar I would be a "sacrificial lamb." Their only hope was that the satellite would keep functioning long enough to give them information by telemetry which would enable them to build a better Telstar II.

If Telstar I had had emotions, it must have felt very insignificant 'way up there, only 34½ inches in diameter, weighing only 170 pounds, and orbiting the earth at a height of between 3,531 and 592 miles. And Telstar I had a hard taskmaster. It was "commanded" to take measurements and report on 112 items each minute, and while doing this, it had to orbit the earth nine times a day. Not only did it have to answer 112 times a minute; it was required to receive and send telephone conversations between the United States and Europe. It is no wonder that the little thing finally went berserk.

First Telstar threw a tantrum. It began giving wrong answers to the scientists at Andover, not because it didn't have the information, but because it was so tired of taking orders — so tired! Then when the scientists ordered it to talk, it refused to answer, and when the engineers told it to be quiet and take a rest, it kept right on talking. Then Telstar refused to send any more television pictures. It continued to send information about radiation in the Van Allen belt, but only when it felt so inclined; and if it wanted to talk all night, the engineers could just sit up and listen. It kept up this behavior for four months, but in February, 1963, Telstar I went silent, and hasn't been heard from since.

The scientists were sorry to see little Telstar go. But it had done a great service in giving them volumes of information on radiation and the Van Allen belts, and it had found there were several effects of the sun, space temperatures, etc. While it didn't know what was wrong with itself, it had given the engineers detailed information, enough for a complete diagnosis of its ills.

Fortunately, to scientists if not to the rest of us,

Telstar I was a fairly simple little thing. It was the space descendant of Sputnik I, and the subsequent satellites. It was a microwave sending and receiving station, much like those on the Kansas prairies, and powered with storage batteries. The rest of its equipment, "crawling" with transistors, was for gathering and measuring data, coding it and sending it back to Andover, Maine.

What caused Telstar's mixed-up behavior and its refusal to obey "commands" was traced to one particular transistor in one of its two command decoders. This made Telstar act like a dog whose ears play him tricks, so when he is commanded to "heel," he hears "sit." Even with this difficulty toward the end, Telstar performed 300 technical tests covering every aspect of transmission, and more than 400 demonstrations proved that a communications satellite was here to stay. It showed that it could handle multichannel telephony, telegraphy, data and telephoto transmission. It telecast fifty transatlantic programs, five of them in color. Two thousand American firms helped make "Humpty-Dumpty" Telstar I, and they knew how to put "Humpty-Dumpty together again," and better.

TELSTAR II

Watching the erratic performance of Telstar I before its complete failure, Bell scientists pinpointed two causes. One of the two command decoders had been affected by radiation. Telstar II must give it better protection. Also Telstar I's transistors used too much current from the storage batteries while the earth shaded its solar cells. But there were other shortcomings which, while not defects, limited Telstar's performance. Greater distance range was the chief need in order to obtain a more exhaustive study of the Van Allen belts.

By late April, 1963, Telstar II was ready for launching. It had been built under the same agreement as was made between NASA and AT&T for launching Telstar I. The first improvement was a better, more powerful Delta rocket which could place Telstar II in orbit with a higher apogee (farthest distance from the earth). Telstar I reached 3,531 miles, while its successor would aim for 6,560. The orbit of Telstar II was lengthened from the previous 158 minutes to 221. This the scientists reckoned would provide longer mutual visibility between Andover and Europe, and probably bring Japan into range, where ground stations were under construction in anticipation of the Olympic Games. For protection from radiation, the decoding transistors were sealed in a vacuum. Telemetry was stepped up to 118 reports per minute. Otherwise the two satellites were nearly identical.

At 7:30 A.M. on May 7, the improved Delta rocket lifted Telstar II from its launching pad at Cape Canaveral (now Cape Kennedy). Everything went exactly as planned, and on schedule. The satellite completed its first orbit of the earth at 11:30 A.M., and telemetry was received at Cape Canaveral and Antigua immediately. At 9:00 P.M. that night, Telstar II transmitted its first television. Thirty-six hours later, a performance by the Apollo Ballet was transmitted to Europe, followed by a talk by AT&T president E. J. MacNeely. In May, 1964, Telstar II was still functioning, and had been joined by satellite Relay.

CONCLUSION

This final chapter on communications must either be short or go on forever. Just as this book was ready for the presses, two new, exciting events in space communications took place. On March 24, 1965, Ranger 9 crashed into Crater Alphonsus on the moon, but not before sending back nearly 7,000 photographs of excellent clarity. These pictures told what the previous Rangers had been unable to convey: the depth of the craters, the steepness of their sides, and the ability of the moon's surface to support the weight of a space vehicle and man. With six RCA cameras Ranger 9 sent its pictures to the Jet Propulsion Laboratory at Goldstone, California, from where they went to our television sets. Ranger 9 was a child of NASA.

On April 6, Comsat's Early Bird went into a preliminary orbit. Last February, Congress authorized the organization of Comsat, a private corporation, closely regulated by the government, to advance the development of satellites for purely commercial use. The eventual plans of Comsat provide for at least four new ground stations, costing in the neighborhood of $170 million.

Now with Early Bird, the first commercial satellite in orbit, messages are going out and coming in from the ground station at Andover, Maine, to and from the ground stations in England, France, and Germany. New stations are soon to be built in Italy and Spain.

Thus, the history of space communication has been one of collaboration between business and government. Telstars I and II were built jointly by NASA and the American Telphone and Telegraph Company. The Telstars' telemetry helped in building the later Rangers. Then government and business pretty much went it alone, although continually exchanging scientific information. Business needed its eighty-five pound, drumshaped Early Bird for business purposes. AT&T needed it for expanded transatlantic telephone communication. Western Union needed it to supplement its transatlantic cables, and the TV networks wished to be in a position to buy British programs and sell some of their own. And what does all of this mean to us, and to our brothers in Greece, Ghana, and Guatamala?

Back in 1930 or thereabouts, that beloved cowboy-humorist Will Rogers said, "I never met a man I didn't like." Will was saying that when you meet a man and really understand him, you can't hate him. The same goes for peoples and nations. If communication, whether by satellites or other media, can bring us to a better understanding of other peoples and nations, and can bring them to understand us better, perhaps therein lies the road to world peace. Arthur Clarke, an English science-fiction writer, twenty years ago foresaw communication satellites and received the usual ridicule aimed at the predictions of science-fiction authors. At the time he said, "Ours will be the last century of the savage, and for all mankind the Stone Age will be over."

Already, space communications have reduced distrust among nations. In a speech made in June, 1964, U.S. Senator Clinton P. Anderson reported, "Recently, Chairman Khrushchev announced that his satellites had photographed U.S. bases. He would be happy, Khrushchev said, 'to show President Johnson my film strips, and President Johnson could show his photographs of Soviet installations taken by U.S. satellites.'" *This only four years after the U-2 incident*. Senator Anderson concluded: "Wherever the Space Age goes, it will bring with it a way of life that encourages tolerance, understanding and a habit of working together."

To put it another way, O. Walter Wagner, in his book *Levels of Brotherhood*, said, "By destruction of distance through mass communication and rapid transportation, the nations of the world have been drawn into an apartment-size civilization. Like the old laundry bag with its concentric ropes — the farther one pulled them, the narrower became the opening of the bag — the farther we extend the lines of communication, the closer we draw together the people of the world."

BIBLIOGRAPHY

Anderson, Clinton P., "Why Leave Earth?," a speech by the U.S. Senator before the 1964 Rotary International Convention, *The Rotarian*, Evansville, Ill., November, 1964.

Bell System, American Telephone and Telegraph Co., *Ten Men and the Telephone; How the Telephone Works; The Telephone in America; The Magic Behind Your Dial;* and *The Story of the Bell Solar Battery* (current pamphlets).

Berril, N. J., *Man's Emerging Mind*, Premier Books, Fawcett World Library, New York, 1962.

Bodmer, Frederick, *The Loom of Language*, Farrar & Rinehart, New York, 1944.

Collins, A. Frederick, *A Bird's Eye View of Invention*, Thomas Y. Crowell Company, New York, 1926.

De Camp, L. Sprague, *The Heroic Age of American Invention*, Doubleday, New York, 1961.

Franklin, Benjamin, *Autobiographical Writings*, selected and edited by Carl Van Doren, Viking Press, New York, 1945.

Halle, Louis J., *Men and Nations*, Princeton University Press, Princeton, N. J., 1962.

Homes, Mrs. Philip B., *Horace Greeley, A Sesqui-Centennial Review*, Vol. XVI, *Historical New Hampshire*, New Hampshire Historical Society, Concord, N.H., 1961.

Hough, Henry Beetle, *Country Editor*, Doubleday, New York, 1940.

Huxley, Aldous, *Tomorrow, and Tomorrow, and Tomorrow*, Harper & Row, New York, 1952.

Jespersen, Otto, *Language, Its Nature, Development and Origin,* MacMillan, New York, 1949.

Linn, William Alexander, *Horance Greeley,* D. Appleton & Company, New York, 1903.

Mencken, H. L., *The American Language,* Alfred A. Knopf, New York, 1937.

Metraux, Guy S., and Crouzet, François, *The Nineteenth Century World,* UNESCO, Mentor Books, New York, 1963.

Moore, Ben Perley, *Reminiscences of Sixty Years in the National Metropolis* (2 vol.), Hubbard Brothers, Philadelphia, 1886.

Mott, Frank Luther, *American Journalism,* The Macmillan Co., New York, 1947.

Muller, Herbert J., *The Loom of History,* Mentor Books, New York, 1958.

Ogg, Oscar, *The 26 Letters,* Thomas Y. Crowell Company New York, 1948.

Partridge, Eric, *Adventures Among Worlds,* Tonbridge Printers, Great Britain, 1961.

Pierce, John R. and David, *Man's World of Sound,* Doubleday, New York, 1958.

Reck, Franklin M., *Radio from Start to Finish,* Thomas Y. Crowell Company, New York, 1942.

Shippen, Katharine B., *Mr. Bell Invents the Telephone,* Random House, New York, 1952.

Sullivan, Mark, *Our Times — The Twenties* (vol. 6), Charles Scribner's Sons, New York, 1935.

Townsend, George Alfred, *Rustics in Rebellion, A Yankee Reporter on the Road to Richmond,* University of North Carolina Press, Chapel Hill, 1950.

Wagner, O. Walter, *Levels of Brotherhood,* United Church Press, Boston, 1964.

Wiley, Charles, *History of the United States,* Collins and Hannay, New York, 1830.

INDEX

217